Hugh Robinson

The Book of 1000 Beautiful Things and Other Favourites

Published by Ballyhay Books,
an imprint of Laurel Cottage Ltd.
Donaghadee, N. Ireland 2003.

Printed by Colour Books Ltd..

ISBN 1 900935 35 X

Foreword

There is the spoken word and there is the written word. Very often they inhabit two entirely separate worlds, but now and again they converge, and in this book, Hugh Robinson makes it happen for us.

Hugh has been a regular contributor to *Love Forty* on BBC Radio Ulster over many years. In the early stages of that relationship his stories were nostalgic pieces looking back to childhood, a childhood of a different age where values were easy to recognise and to understand. That gave them immediate appeal to a very wide audience of those who, like myself, feel that the world is now a less friendly, less comfortable place.

From those beginnings, Hugh's broadcasts have broadened to include both fact and fiction, and the world is now his canvas. His is the art of good communication. I know this from the encouraging response to every broadcast he has made.

And here, again, is the translation from the spoken to the printed word. Here are experiences and writing which will give a great deal of pleasure to all who read his stories. Long may he continue to produce them.

Walter Love

Contents

Introduction

Following the success of my first volume for Ballyhay Books, *Back Across the Fields of Yesterday*, that book has gone into reprint. It has been most gratifying for me as a writer to have received so many letters and phone calls from readers expressing their delight as they shared with me memories of childhood country life in County Down just after the war. It seems my writings brought to the surface for many people their own treasured memories of happier times when life was slower and more simple, people were kinder, and both town and countryside abounded with colourful characters we never see now. Best of all, laughter was never far away, whatever the circumstances.

I received many requests to produce another book in similar vein. Fortunately, there was no scarcity of material. *Back Across the Fields of Yesterday* was largely autobiographical and in the main I stuck to the more or less factual events of my childhood. In this new work, *The Book of One Thousand Beautiful Things and Other Favourites*, I have the opportunity to bring together in one volume all my other material which has proved so popular on my BBC Radio broadcasts with Walter Love and on my Storytelling Evenings. And of course my most popular story, *The Book of One Thousand Beautiful Things* is here produced in its full and unabridged version.

The theme of Part One in this volume is a blend of more childhood memories, observations of the good old Northern Ireland and Southern Ireland characters with a bit of pure Irish blarney tossed in for good measure. I hope in this section many readers will say - as they did about my previous book - "I knew people just like that. But their names were ..." The characters include street urchins and tramps, tough old schoolmasters, bachelors who never seem to have any luck, farmers and often time the spirit of Christmas itself. The backdrops are Smithfield Market and the back streets of Belfast in the hungry thirties, lonely cottages on mysterious Christmas Eves, dance halls and pubs, snowy Belfast Christmases and a bit of old Ireland in which no one but the imagination of the author and the characters in his story have ever dwelled. Although most of the pieces in this part of the book are mainly fictional there is more than a grain of truth, and of myself, in each of them. Some are very much aligned to events in my own life. Just how much I will leave to the readers imagination.

As a writer, I work best from personal experience, believing what comes from the heart will go to the heart. Recently, in my more mature years, I have begun to experience some very beautiful things in my life – rare and lovely happenings which were indeed the fulfilment of – I dare not use the word dreams for I never even dreamt these things could ever be – but perhaps fantasies which a child might hold and believe that one day they may indeed come to pass. Part Two is given over to these factual experiences and dear people who have come to mean so much to me in my later life, every bit as meaningful and tender and precious as my beloved childhood upon which I expend so much ink. These people and places and events are unique and beautiful in themselves and deserve in their own merit to have a voice. I consider myself privileged to bring them to a wider audience within these pages and to satisfy those of my radio audience who have asked for them to be made available in the printed word. The book closes with *Why I Love Her*, a little tribute to the places and people of all Ireland, and which received an overwhelming response when I was invited to read it on three consecutive mornings on BBC Radio Ulster.

Many readers kindly told me they laughed and cried their way through *Back Across the Fields of Yesterday*. I hope I will enable them to do the same as they turn the pages of *The Book of 1000 Beautiful Things and Other Favourites.*

Hugh Robinson
Newtownards 2003

Part I

The Storyteller

Look, then into thy heart, and write.

Longfellow

The Book of One Thousand Beautiful Things

"How much is the book, mister?"

Billy McCullough stood on tiptoes and peered anxiously over the pile of musty smelling books and comics and magazines in Barney's Smithfield Secondhand Bookshop. *Picture Post, Tit-Bits, Everybody's, Playbox* and several assorted *Dandy* and *Beano*, jumbled up with battered copies of Dickens, Tolstoy, Hardy, Homer and Annie S. Swan and Sherlock Holmes.

Billy had never seen so many books in one place. Never. Why hadn't he stumbled on this place before? Books everywhere, all shapes and sizes, squeezed tightly into packed shelves or built in tall wobbling piles which reached from the floor to the ceiling. Half a dozen cardboard boxes each holding an assortment of less valued volumes were tied up roughly with a piece of coarse twine and stacked in a corner. Some books were tied up in bundles without the benefit of a cardboard box. The poorest relations of all, a dozen or so volumes of nothing in particular, and which appeared to have smuggled themselves into the shop when no-one was looking, lay scattered forlornly about the floor. The possibility of being elevated to a position of honour on the bookshelves, or even taking their chances somewhere in the swaying skyscraper of volumes, seemed remote. Not even worthy of a piece of string, the hapless books suffered the ignominy of being kicked and trodden on by every snow-covered boot which entered the shop. Billy was one of the few who treated the castaways on the floor with respect. He had threaded his way through them carefully, taking care not to damage any as he'd made his way over to the skinny little man behind the counter. Now he shuffled along a little bit farther so he could see the man better and without having to stand on tiptoes.

"How much is it, mister? How much is the book?"

Barney, a balding shifty looking man with the stub of a pencil behind one ear and the butt of a Woodbine cigarette behind the other remained motionless on his stool behind the counter. His beady little eyes devoured the print in his Zane Grey western, his thin lips silently mouthing each word as he read it. Barney liked westerns. And he liked Zane Grey best of all. The cowboys Zane Grey wrote about were two-fisted, two-gun, straight-shooting hombres who were more than a match for any of the black-hatted baddies who had the misfortune to tangle with them. Billy waited patiently until Barney, tracing the lines of print with a nicotine stained finger, finished a paragraph and pulled the pencil stub from behind his ear. The man licked the blunt lead with his tongue and underlined the last word he'd read. It was a clever little device he'd perfected for his own convenience. Made it easier to find the place when you came back after attending to a customer. It was only the second mark he'd made in the book all day.

Barney stuck the pencil back behind his ear and rose from his seat. He frowned. He didn't often get kids this age in here. And especially not at Christmas time. They were too busy trailing round the big shops looking at Hoppalong Cassidy cowboy outfits and wind-up train sets and seeing what they could knock off.

If they came into the market at all it was usually just to swear at the parrot in Francie's pet shop or feed bits of soap to the monkey. But they didn't come in here. Kids didn't read books. And even if this one did, he didn't have two h'pennies to rub together. You could tell that from his thin grey jersey, ragged and torn and not enough material in it to keep out the glistening wet snow seeping through to his skin.

Billy was conscious of the man's sceptical gaze. It didn't deter him. He repeated his question for the third time.

"How much is the book, mister?"

Barney sniffed in irritation and tossed the Zane Grey on to a pile of *Illustrated* magazines.

"What book, son? What book are you talkin' about?"

"This one!" Billy answered quickly, encouraged he had finally captured the little man's attention. He tapped the blue hardback with his forefinger and laid it down in front of Barney. "That one, mister. *The Book of One Thousand Beautiful Things*! How much is it?"

Barney picked up the volume disinterestedly. Whatever the price, the kid couldn't afford it. He wiped the dust from the cover with the sleeve of his jacket and squinted at the faded gold lettering on the spine. *The Book of One Thousand Beautiful Things*. By Arthur Mee. He sniffed and ran the back of his hand across his mouth. He'd never heard tell of it. Or Arthur Mee either. Must've picked it up in a job lot somewhere. Probably in that big house he emptied up the Malone Road a couple of weeks ago. You never knew what you were going to find in the big houses. You'd be surprised. Trouble was, it was hard stuff to shift. All that high-falootin caboodle nobody could understand and nobody wanted.

A quick flick through the pages revealed nothing of interest. Poetry. Pictures of old paintings. Quotations from the Bible. Bits of Shakespeare. Not the sort of stuff he usually carried. Too slow. *Maria Marten and Murder at the Red Barn* or Sexton Blake or

Zane Grey. That was the stuff to give the troops. They usually came back for more of that. But Arthur Mee?

"Great book that, son," enthused Barney, spitting on the cover and giving a particularly stubborn piece of dirt a bit of a rub. "Arthur Mee wrote it y'know. Great writer. You knew what you were doin' when you picked that up. Not many of his books knockin' about Belfast. Have you got any of his stuff?"

Billy shook his head. "We have no books in our house, mister. My da' says readin' doesn't put any money in your pocket."

Barney sniffed disdainfully. Talk like that could put a fella out of business. And business was bad enough this Christmas with the gantries in the shipyard rusted red and the half of Belfast tramping the streets looking for work. It wasn't easy to sell books. Most people hadn't enough money to buy the *War Cry*. He was still trying to formulate a telling response as Billy eased the book from his hands and slowly turned the pages. He stopped near the back of the book and traced a line of print with his finger. He pushed the volume back toward Barney and pointed to the sentence.

"How do you say that, mister? And what does it mean?"

Barney's little eyes took off across the page, never blinking, but never still for an instant. Backward and forward across the print they scurried, up and down, sometimes shifting from the first line to the last, then back again to pick up the words in the middle. The man's soft little face, pointed nose and darting eyes, reminded Billy of the tiny mouse his mother had wanted him to kill when she'd captured it in the corner of the scullery a couple of days earlier. Like the mouse, the man sat motionless, except for the impatient little eyes twinkling and racing all over the page of print. Billy hadn't the heart to kill the mouse. So he'd chased it out through the hole in the bottom of the back door. He'd forgotten all about it until now. He thought it strange the little man's face should remind him of the mouse. But it did.

"That's poetry, son," declared Barney when he finally looked up. "Ye Banks and Braes O' Bonny Doon. Very famous. A fella called Rabbie Burns writ that. Years ago. In a pub. In Glasgow."

"Ye Banks and Braes O' Bonny Doon!" Billy breathed the words in an almost silent whisper, as if they were a magical incantation. His big blue eyes opened wide in wonderment as he slowly repeated the words. "Ye Banks and Braes O' Bonny Doon! But what does that mean, mister? What's a brae? And what's Bonny Doon?"

Barney snorted and tossed the book down on the counter. Poetry wasn't his strong point, and he wasn't afraid to admit it. He only sold the stuff. He didn't have to understand it as well. But that was the trouble with poets. You never knew what they were on about. And especially the Scotch ones. They were the worst of the lot. All that braw brichct moonlichct nichct stuff. You might as well try to understand double-dutch as make any sense out of all that nonsense.

"How do I know what it means! That was writ years ago. Nobody talks like that now. Not round here anyway."

Billy rescued the book from the pile of reading matter on the counter and wiped the remains of Barney's spittle away with the cuff of his jersey. He was disappointed the man couldn't tell him what a brae was and what Bonny Doon was. He thought the man would have read all the books in his bookshop and known everything there was to know about everyone of them. And especially this one. This was a good book. He knew it was.

"Well, how much is it, mister? How much is *The Book of One Thousand Beautiful Things*?"

Barney pulled the Woodbine butt from behind his ear. He stuck it in his mouth and fumbled about for a match. When he found one he lit up, wheezing and coughing as he blew a cloud of hazy grey smoke to the ceiling. You had to give the kid credit. He was a tryer. Didn't have a h'penny to his name. But he was a tryer. He took another drag from the Woodbine and shook his head.

"Too dear for you, son. I'd be lookin' a shillin' for that. Couldn't take a penny less." He lifted a pile of torn comics from the end of the counter and slapped them down in front of Billy. "What about them? *Funny Wonder. Rainbow.* And *Billy Bunter.* I'll give you six for a penny. Keep you readin' over Christmas. What d'ye say?"

Billy picked up a copy of the *Rainbow.* He gazed half-heartedly at the funny little cartoon characters and the balloons of conversation issuing from their mouths. The characters were an assortment of ducks, giraffes, badgers and clowns all dressed in clothes of bright red and green and yellow. They all seemed to be having a wonderful time. Billy laid the comic down and gazed at Barney.

"I like them comics, mister. But I'd rather have *The Book of One Thousand Beautiful Things*." He hesitated. "Would you take a jam pot for it mister? My da' says he used to get into the pictures to see Charlie Chaplin for a jam pot."

Barney rolled his eyes heavenward and groaned as he took a last despairing suck on the remains of the glowing weed in his mouth. Billy thought the man was going to swallow the burning tobacco right down his throat. But Barney removed the butt just as it began to singe his lips. He stubbed it out on the *Rainbow* comic and leaned low over the counter so his face was directly opposite Billy's.

"No, son! I would not take a jam pot for it! What would I do with a jam pot! Your da' might have got into the flicks for a jam pot when he was a kid. But he wouldn't get in now. It'll cost him two dee to get into Joe McKibben's - and Joe's is the cheapest picture house in town." He straightened up. "Why don't you get your oul' fella to buy you the book? For Christmas?"

It was a stupid suggestion and Barney knew it before he had finished speaking. If the kid's da' had any dough he might have been able to put some clothes on the youngster's back.

"My da's on relief," answered Billy. "He's out concretin' the streets. For a food voucher. He couldn't buy it."

Barney nodded. "Thought as much. No money comin' in, eh?"

He picked up *The Book of One Thousand Beautiful Things* and flicked through the pages again, wondering if window cleaning might be a more profitable proposition than bookselling. All you needed was a bucket of water and a lump of cloth. No shop. No books. No overheads. No worries. Just a bucket of water and a lump of cloth. It was worth thinking about.

"Tell you what, son. Gimme tenpence and the book's yours. All wrapped up for Christmas." He spread his arms out in an appealing gesture of goodwill. "I can't say fairer than that. At this rate I'll be out concretin' the streets with your da'. Then we'll all be starvin'. At tenpence I'm givin' it away. I'm givin' it away."

Billy's eyes widened as the prospect of owning the book suddenly became more of a reality. Tenpence was an awful lot of money, more than he ever had in his whole life. But it wasn't as much as a shilling. Maybe he could get tenpence. Somewhere. He nodded his head up and down vigorously.

"Okay, mister. I'll take it."

Barney stared at the boy, his mouth dropping open in surprise.

"You'll take it, son? For tenpence?"

Billy nodded. "Yes mister. For tenpence."

Barney reached the book across the counter with one hand and held out the other for the cash. Things were looking up. Maybe he would be able to pay the rent this week after all. "There you are son. The best tenpence worth you'll ever buy. Arthur Mee wrote it y'know. You've got a real investment there."

Billy stepped back quickly from the counter. "But I haven't got the money yet, mister. Will you keep it for me? 'Til I get the money?"

Barney rolled his eyes and groaned again. The window cleaning was becoming more attractive by the minute. Why was he wasting his time with this kid who had as much chance of getting tenpence as he had of winning the Irish Sweepstake? The grass was knee high in the shipyard. Grown men tramping the streets of Belfast hadn't got tenpence to their name and no chance of getting it. He looked away from Billy, trying to avoid the blue eyes pleading silently and making him feel so uncomfortable. He tossed the book on to the counter and made a mental note never to enter into conversation with a customer until he had at least seen the colour of his money. He had to get this kid out of his shop before he went nuts.

"Okay kid. I'll hold it for you. But don't be too long about gettin' the dough. There's not another one of them books in the whole of Belfast. Arthur Mee's stuff is hard to get. Big demand for it."

Billy's eyes gleamed. "Aw thanks! Thanks a million mister! I'll get the money. Don't you worry about it." He picked up the book and ran his fingers gently over the cover as if he were stroking a kitten. "I'll get the money, mister. Don't you worry."

Billy laid the book gently down on the counter. He took one last lingering look at the battered volume. Then he turned and picked his way across the book-strewn floor toward the door and snowy Gresham Street. It was then Barney saw the boy's feet. They were bare. They were dirty. And they were blue with cold.

Barney sighed, a long deep mournful and audible sigh. "Hey kid! Hold on a minute!"

Billy turned. He bit his lip. Had the man changed his mind? Would he not let him have the book? For tenpence?

"Yes, mister?"

Barney picked up *The Book of One Thousand Beautiful Things*. He turned the pages. "Look at this, son. Do you see where some of them pages is tattered and tore? And look at the state of that cover. I might have a bit of trouble sellin' that book. I get a lot of high-class customers in here. Like their books to be in mint condition." He pursed his lips and frowned deeply, fusing his bushy grey eyebrows together. "Tell you what. Make it ninepence. Do you think you could get ninepence?"

Ninepence! Billy could hardly believe his luck. He was nearly sure he could get ninepence. Somewhere. It would be easier to get than tenpence. "Aw thanks mister! Thanks a million! I'll come back. When I get the money!" He turned away. His head was already swimming with ideas how to raise the nine pennies as he opened the door and walked out into Gresham Street. He stuck his hands into his short trouser pockets and held his head high, as if he already owned *The Book of One Thousand Beautiful Things*. Billy whistled a snatch from Phil the Fluter's Ball as he passed the pet shop with the black and white rabbits and the baldy monkey. He strode determinedly past the piles of second-hand furniture and faded paintings of wild deer in misty mountains in the Highlands of Scotland. He gazed up at the faces of all the people who passed him by. He wanted to stop every one of them and tell them all about *The Book of One Thousand Beautiful Things* and that soon the book would be his. He slowed and stopped as he drew level with an old man sharpening knives on a big spinning grindstone. Billy watched in fascination as the old man pushed the treadle of the contraption up and down with his foot and the stone spun round and round and the dancing orange sparks leapt high into the air as the Sheffield Steel was applied to the rim of the stone. The old man looked up and caught Billy's eye. He smiled. Billy smiled. Then Billy turned away, murmuring softly, over and over again, "Ye Banks and Braes O' Bonny Doon...Ye Banks and Braes O' Bonny Doon..."

Milligan's School, named after its solitary teacher, got out at three o'clock. Billy could hardly wait. He sat in his place in the long wooden desk, his face propped in his hands, staring blankly at the big clock above the blackboard. He watched the brass pendulum swinging to and fro in perpetual motion. Something was wrong. The spidery black hands on the clock were stuck. They were stuck at two minutes to three. Billy stared at the hands, hard, with all the concentration he could muster, willing them to make one last effort, move, and reach the appointed time when freedom came. Why was it you could never see the clock hands move? No matter how hard you watched them, you couldn't see them move, and the more you watched them the less they moved.

These two minutes were proving to be the longest of the whole day. Billy had spent the entire afternoon suffering heavy blows on the head and cruel words of insult from Mr Milligan because he didn't know his eleven times table. Billy didn't care. He hadn't the slightest interest in the eleven times table or any other tables or sums of any sort. There wasn't any magic in sums – or arithmetic, as Mr Milligan called them. They always added up to the same thing. Three and three always made six. If it didn't, there was something wrong. And there was usually something wrong when Billy did the adding up. You either knew how to do sums or you didn't. It was as simple as that. But you couldn't change them or turn them into something else, the way you could with words. You could use the same words over and over again and always get a different story or learn something new - something you hadn't known before. Like Ye Banks' and Braes O' Bonny Doon. He'd never heard tell of Ye Banks and Braes O' Bonny Doon until yesterday when he found the book in the bookshop. And he still didn't know what it meant. But he'd find out when he owned *The Book of One Thousand Beautiful Things*. And he'd find out a lot of other things as well.

Billy traced a finger into the initials some long departed scholar had cut deep into the wooden desk. Would the bucket still be where he'd hidden it? Hiding the bucket had been a great idea. It meant he didn't have to go the whole way back home to pick it up after school. If he got started right away he might get the bucket filled before dark.

"McCullough!" The angry rasp of Mr Milligan's gravel voice - a mighty roar – abruptly interrupted Billy's daydream. He sat bolt upright. The teacher hurled a box of chalks at him in a final act of frustration. Billy ducked and the box ricocheted off his desk and bounced into the corner and burst open. "McCullough!" roared Mr Milligan, "you will be delighted to know that all further attempts to knock some degree of knowledge into your thick skull have now ceased for the day!" The teacher rose from his desk and slammed its lid shut with a force which made Billy blink in alarm as the possibility of further violence threatened. "You, McCullough, and the rest of this rag-bag of the great unlearned are now free to return with all haste to the jungle from whence you came!"

Billy was first through the school gate. It was a bitterly cold Belfast day and a stinging spiteful rain lashed down. Billy didn't care. He sprinted along Manor Street, splashing through the puddles and ignoring the ginger and white mongrel which sped along after him and snapped at his bare feet. The dog gave up the chase at the junction of the Oldpark and turned to seek new sport. Billy kept running on down Albertville Drive. He didn't stop until he reached the Crumlin Road.

Billy finally halted. He leaned heavily against a lamp post. Bent almost double with exhaustion he pulled in great gulps of air to his aching lungs. His grey jersey and trousers dripped water and they clung heavily and uncomfortably to his sweating body. He looked up at the miserable sky. Maybe the task was too big. Maybe he couldn't get ninepence. Maybe he should just abandon his great plan and the whole idea and go home. He turned his head as a tram droned toward him on tracks gleaming silver in the rain.

The tram's interior lights were full on although it wasn't yet dark. It looked warm and cosy inside. It might be worthwhile pinching a ride on the tram. And then again, it might not. The last time he'd pinched a ride on a tram there'd been a peeler on board and he'd been lucky to get away with a clip around the ear and the promise of six months up the Crumlin if he did it again. And he couldn't afford to go to jail now. The man wouldn't keep *The Book of One Thousand Beautiful Things* for six months. He wouldn't keep it that long.

Billy wiped the rain from his face and watched the tram draw level with him and rumble past. He grinned. He could run as fast as that. Easily. He took a deep breath and sprinted after the tram. He caught it and passed it and didn't stop running until he reached the piece of waste ground where he'd hidden the bucket near Vistula Street. He clambered in among the piles of rubble and dirt and household rubbish and rotten rags and began to dig with his hands. He pulled away a rusted red lump of corrugated iron and closed his fingers on the handle of the bucket. He heaved a sigh of relief and pulled the bucket out from the rubbish. If somebody had found the bucket and stolen it his plan would have been ruined. But it was safe. Now he could really begin the first part of his great idea to raise the money for *The Book of One Thousand Beautiful Things*. He looked up. The rain was easing. By the time he'd walked up the entry and round the corner to number one Vistula Street it had ceased completely and his sticky steamy clothes no longer bothered him.

Billy set his iron bucket down on the doorstep of Number One, Vistula Street. Taking a deep breath he lifted a hand and knocked timidly on the closed door. He didn't like knocking on the doors of people he didn't know. And he didn't like asking them to give him something for nothing, even if it was only some stale bread or a rotten potato or whatever food refuse they might have. But he had to do it. There wasn't any response to his knock. He lifted his hand again, to knock a little louder, but the door suddenly swung open. The old, very old woman who opened it, reminded Billy of a witch he'd once seen in a *Lot-O-Fun* comic. For an instant he thought it was the same witch. The old woman's face was deeply and horribly wrinkled with the same lines of pale loose skin as the witch, and like the witch, she didn't have any teeth. A black shawl was pulled carelessly over the woman's long white hair and thin shoulders. Was she a witch?

"Any - any skins, m-missus?" stuttered Billy uncomfortably. "Potato skins? Stale bread? Any refuse at all?" He stared at the woman's hideous sunken features and studied the single white hair curling from the centre of her chin. Why was she making those awful chewing movements with her mouth when it was plain to see she hadn't anything to chew, and even if she did, she hadn't any teeth to chew it with? She was a witch. He knew she was. Was she trying to put a spell on him? Suddenly Billy wanted to drop his bucket and run. But he remembered *The Book of One Thousand Beautiful Things*. He stood his ground. "Any scraps at all, missus?"

The old woman stopped chewing, her mouth half open. She definitely didn't have teeth. The grey watery eyes stared at Billy, almost without seeing him. Suddenly she reached out a bony white arm and grabbed the bucket and without saying a word retreated backwards into the dark hall. Billy watched her disappear. He waited for what seemed a very long time. He waited even longer then peered around the door, trying to see the old woman in the darkness at the end of the hall. She wasn't there. She wasn't coming back. She'd stolen his bucket to mix her magic potions . All witches needed a good iron pot or a bucket to mix their magic potions in. She'd stolen his bucket. Then, suddenly, the old woman was standing before him.

"There ye are son," she cackled in a thin breathless voice as she reached Billy the bucket. "That'll help ye to get the picture-money." The toothless smile and the pat on the head were meant to encourage. They only served to make Billy step sharply back from the old woman's touch. He took the bucket and stared into it, expecting to see a collection of mutilated toads and snake's heads. That was the sort of stuff witches usually kept about them. But there wasn't any of that. Just two or three pieces of potato skin partially covered by a single decaying cabbage leaf and swirling about in a drop of soured milk which smelt awful. Billy knew M'Crory paid a top rate of a penny- h'penny for a bucket of good pig-swill. Suddenly *The Book of One Thousand Beautiful Things* seemed a long, long way away.

"Thanks, missus. I'll call again."

The sky leadened and the rain came again, slashing, sleety, hard, hurtful rain. It was dark and Billy was cold and wet and miserable when the bucket was finally filled. Wearily he sank down beneath a lamp post in Harrison Street with the bucket of foul-smelling pig-swill beside him. He rested his arms across the top of the bucket and lowered his head on the pillow they made. He didn't care about the rain which dripped from his clothes and soaked his skin. He didn't care about the bitter cold which nipped his fingers and chilled his feet. He didn't care about the hardness and wetness of the kerb beneath him. He only wanted to rest his aching arms and legs and close his eyes. Just for a little while. Then he'd set out on the journey home.

Billy almost fell asleep across the bucket of pig-swill. He probably would have drifted off into unconsciousness if it hadn't been for the sound of the bicycle bell. He lifted his head slowly as he caught a glimpse of the old man turning his ancient bicycle into Harrison Street. The man pedalled the bicycle erratically over the cobblestones toward where Billy sat. He dismounted and laid his bicycle against the lamp post.

Billy had seen Joe do it a hundred times. But he watched again. He loved to see the magic Joe performed in the dark Belfast streets with the gas lamps. The old man took the long wooden pole secured at the side of his bicycle and offered it up to the glass globe at the top of the lamp post He flicked his wrist and pulled gently on the ring of the chain where it dangled from its pivoted arm. The magic happened. Billy smiled and his eyes danced as he watched the white mantle inside the lamp ignite in a white fluorescent glow. The warm light spilled on to the black gleaming wet cobblestones and transformed the dark puddles at Billy's feet into pools of liquid gold. The featureless spits of hard rain shafting down past the gas lamp were suddenly shining cascades of golden needles.

Joe nodded at the bucket.

"Tryin' to get the money for a couple of fegs, son?"

Billy smiled and shook his head.

"Not fegs, Joe. A book. I'm goin' to buy a book. *The Book of One Thousand Beautiful Things*."

"A book," repeated Joe, as he secured the long pole to the bar of his bicycle. "You're a man after my own heart, son. A blessed companion is a book. Aye. A blessed companion is a book." He pulled the bicycle away from the lamp post and wagged a finger at Billy. "You're doin' the right thing, son. Get knowledge. Get learnin'. And get wisdom. Above all, get wisdom." He threw his leg over his bicycle and pedalled away into the darkness, leaving Billy staring after him, trying to remember and make sense of the old lamplighter's words. But Joe's words were too deep for him. He sighed and dragged himself to his feet. He lifted his bucket of refuse and tipped it over, just enough to drain off the rain-water and dirty liquid which overflowed the rim. He watched the gold splash away and disappear from the pool at his feet as the dirty wet sludge emptied into it. He lifted his bucket, turned, and trudged wearily into the darkness and drizzling rain.

The bell above Mrs M'Gilton's wee shop in Cree Street cling-clanged sweetly as Billy pushed his way inside. He held the penny-h'penny McCrory had given him for the bucket of pig-swill tightly in his closed fist. Billy loved the smell of Mrs M'Gilton's wee shop. He was never quite sure what the smell was, but he loved it just the same. Once he'd thought it came from the American apples. As big as a man's fist they were, crimson red and shining like a billiard ball, so shiny he imagined Mrs M'Gilton polished them every morning before she opened her little shop. On another occasion he thought the liquorice allsorts were responsible, and one day he was almost certain it was the toffee apples glued in their tray of sticky syrup that was giving off the intoxicating aroma. This choice was then discarded in favour of the cigarettes – Turf, Woodbine, Pasha, Craven A and Gallaghers Blues – lined up on the shelf behind Mrs M'Gilton. And it could have been the tea lying loose in the wooden silver-lined tea-chest on the floor at the end of the counter. But Billy decided it wasn't any one of these. It was all of them, blending together to produce the mysterious delicious aroma. He breathed in deeply, holding his breath, savouring the sweetness of it all as Mrs M'Gilton shuffled in from her back kitchen.

Mrs M'Gilton was as spick and span as her little shop and the tiny dab of French perfume – genuine French perfume – she wore behind each ear, added yet another fragrance to the already heady scent of the room. She straightened a box of Mrs Cullen's Headache Powders beside the tray of toffee apples. She smiled at Billy.

"Good morning, Billy. What can I get you?"

Billy pursed his lips. He feasted his eyes and his taste buds on the toffee apples and the big bottle of brandy balls at the other side of the headache powders. His eyes strayed to the nougat bars, pink and white and chewy. He liked nougat. The only trouble with nougat was it stuck in your teeth and made your jaws sore when you tried to tear a lump off. But it lasted a long time. Gobstoppers lasted a long time too, even longer than nougat. But the flavour wasn't as good. And they could break your teeth. He'd broken one of his back teeth trying to split a gobstopper in two. Maybe the black liquorice pipes with their little red dabs of red flame on the bowl would be the best value of all. He could have any of these. And that didn't make the decision he had to make any easier. He rubbed the penny- h'penny between his finger and thumb. For an instant he weakened in favour of the toffee apples. Then he thought of *The Book of One Thousand Beautiful Things*.

"Would you have an empty orange box, Mrs M'Gilton?"

Mrs M'Gilton smiled again. "No. I haven't. But I'll soon empty one." She disappeared under the counter and came up again with an armful of oranges which immediately caused Billy to believe he had at last traced the source of the secret nectar in Mrs M'Gilton's shop. Mrs M'Gilton built the seven oranges in a pyramid between the toffee apples and the burnished brass scales and then ducked behind the counter one more time. She popped up again with a large box of wooden slats held together with wire and staples. She set it on the counter and wiped her hands on her dark Paisley-pattern apron.

"There you are, Billy. Will that do?"

Billy nodded. "It's bigger than I thought, Mrs M'Gilton." He hesitated. "Will it still be a penny-h'penny?"

"A penny-h'penny it is, Billy. Always the same price for you. Are you going to do a wee bit of work?"

Billy laid the penny-h'penny down beside the toffee apples. "I'm tryin' to get the money for a book, Mrs M'Gilton."

"Oh? What book?"

"*The Book of One Thousand Beautiful Things*. Arthur Mee wrote it. There's only one of them in the whole of Ireland."

Mrs M'Gilton shook her head slowly from side to side. "I never heard of Arthur Mee. Annie S. Swan's my favourite. She writes lovely books. But I'm sure that book of yours is a good one too. You'll have to let me see it when you get it." She dipped a hand into the jar of brandy balls and pulled one out. She handed it to Billy. "There you are, Billy. That'll keep you warm while you're working. And I hope you get your book."

Billy took the brandy ball and slipped it into his pocket. He picked up his orange box. "Thanks Mrs M'Gilton. Thanks a million."

Mrs M'Gilton smiled, a warm smile. "You're welcome. You're more than welcome, son."

The bell above the door in Mrs M'Gilton's wee sweet shop cling-clanged sweetly as Billy staggered into the street with his giant orange box. All he had to do now was find a hatchet.

Billy hadn't reckoned it would have taken so long to chop the box into neat bundles of firewood. The problem was the wire. And the staples. Most orange boxes were just nailed together with solid little blocks of wood at each corner. It was easy to knock them apart. This orange box had been held together with lengths of wire secured to the wood by a couple of dozen staples.

The wire had to be removed before he could even begin his work properly. And he wanted to do it properly.

Billy understood the secret of making a good bundle of sticks. It wasn't any good just smashing the box to bits and pulling the wire away and tying up the pieces of wood any old way. Every stick had to be a certain length, not too short, and not too long so it wouldn't fit into the grate. And they had to be more or less the correct thickness. Too thick and they wouldn't light. Too thin and they'd flare up immediately and burn away like a piece of paper. If you made a bundle like that you'd never sell another one at the same house. Neat, tidy bundles of sticks, proper size and proper thickness. That's what he needed.

And he'd done it. He'd eased the staples, every one of them, individually, away from the wood, with the point of a rusty nail. He'd pulled the wire away, leaving the box free and clean and ready for the hatchet. He'd chopped the sticks into bundles, tied them tightly and sold them, six bundles at a penny a bundle. Sixpence. He'd never had sixpence. Sixpence was a lot of money. But it wasn't enough. He needed ninepence and now it was raining again, sheeting down and swirling along Royal Avenue, then twisting and turning into York Street and stinging his face and numbing his cheeks.

Billy didn't care about the rain. He strode jauntily along York Street, his Jackie Coogan cap perched on his head at a ridiculous angle. The cap was two sizes too big. That didn't bother Billy. The cap was there to give him some protection from the teeming rain. That was its sole purpose and function, and it was doing a good job. His feet were cold. And wet. That was nothing new. But his head was dry as he cheerily jingled the six copper pennies in his right-hand trouser pocket - the one without the hole. It would take more than a little rain to dampen his spirits today. Soon, very soon, *The Book of One Thousand Beautiful Things* would be his.

York Street was always busy on a Friday afternoon and with Christmas almost here Belfast was a bustling city, its citizens hunting about for what scraps of Christmas cheer they could afford. Billy was glad the rain hadn't driven everyone off the streets. He needed people on the streets. The more people, the easier it would be for him to raise the final three pennies he needed to buy *The Book of One Thousand Beautiful Things*.

The sudden sharp crack of a horsewhip across the street made him look up. An Inglis breadserver seated high up on his cab clip-clopped his horse smartly along the wet road, heading toward Eliza Street and home. Another nag, more ancient of days and something less in the way of pedigree, tossed its head and snorted great clouds of steaming breath into the air, protesting vainly against the heavy load of coal brick it was obliged to haul in and out of the little back streets. Billy kicked an empty cigarette carton away into the river of water flowing down the road at the side of the kerbstones. He looked up quickly as he heard the sound he wanted to hear.

Stumpy Watson stood where he always stood, right on the corner of York Street and Donegal Street, bawling in that indecipherable voice given exclusively to and interpreted only by fellow newsboys. Despite the fact no one could really understand the word shouted intermittently by Stumpy, they knew without a doubt he was selling Belfast Telegraphs at that very spot.

Billy sprinted up to Stumpy and watched in admiration as his friend vocalized a particularly fine "Teleeee-a-sixaaa" which cracked even louder than the breadserver's whip around the busy junction. Stumpy prided himself he had the best "Teleeee-a-sixaaa" in the whole of Belfast.

"Hiya B-B-Billy," chortled Stumpy. "W-what ye d-d-doin' down here on a d-d-day like this? I thought you were g-goin' to the p-pictures to see the D-D-Dead End Kids!"

Billy grinned up at Stumpy, a mischievous little grin.

"Changed m' mind, Stumpy. I'm workin'. How much is your Telegraphs?"

"P-penny-h'penny," advised Stumpy, who stood nearly six foot tall and was as broad as a brush shaft. "D-d-d'ye want one?"

Billy shook his head as his grin grew wider. "Not me! How much do you pay for them, Stumpy?"

"Penny," responded Stumpy quickly as he whipped a paper from under his arm and proffered it to a well-dressed gent with an umbrella and trilby hat. Billy watched wide-eyed as the man gave Stumpy two pennies and waved away the change. Stumpy dropped the money into his pocket and wiped away a drop which had taken up residence at the end of his nose. He looked down as Billy tugged his sleeve.

"Where do you get them, Stumpy? Where do you get the Telegraphs?"

Stumpy exchanged another newspaper for two coins and turned his attention back to the youngster. "Y-you want to go into b-business for yourself. D-don't ye?"

Billy nodded eagerly, his grin growing broader by the moment.

"Well," said Stumpy, "you'll get the p-papers round at the Hole in Li-Library Street." He poked a long bony finger in Billy's chest. "But listen. If you're g-goin' to flog Teles, don't be comin' near my p-pitch. It's hard enough makin' a ta-tanner without you buttin' in."

Billy didn't hear the last piece of advice. He was already passing the Telegraph office and turning into Library Street. He was disappointed to find the Hole wasn't really a hole, just a dark gateway leading to the despatch end of the newspaper building. A rough wooden bench piled high with inky newspapers barred any further progress. A couple of newsboys, not much older than himself, grabbed their papers from the weary looking man behind the bench and pushed past him out to the city streets.

Billy waited patiently until it was his turn. Smiling, he spread his six pennies on the bench. The man peeled off six Telegraphs and pushed them toward him, without speaking. Billy lifted his newspapers and stuck them under his arm, just the way Stumpy did.

"I'm goin' to buy *The Book of One Thousand Beautiful Things*," he informed the man behind the counter. "Did you ever read it, mister?"

The man hauled a bundle of papers from the ground and heaved them on to the table. He took a puff on his pipe and shook his head. "Niver heard tell of it. But I don't read much. I'm a domino man."

Billy frowned. How could a man who didn't read very much get a job selling newspapers?

"You should read it, mister. It's all about Ye Banks and Braes O' Bonny Doon and things like that. But there's only one of them in the whole world. And I'm goin' to buy it. The man in Smithfield is goin' to keep it for me. 'Til I get the money." Billy lifted the papers a bit higher under his arm and turned toward the street. Then he stopped and looked back.

"Mister?"

"What?"

"Arthur Mee wrote it, y'know."

Selling the Telegraphs would be easy. Real easy. And the best place to sell them would be Corn Market. Corn Market was always filled with people, even on a wet day like this. Five different streets led into the circle of space right in the centre of the city. He would have the papers sold in next to no time. This was an even better spot than where Stumpy sold his papers and he wondered why Stumpy didn't come down here. He debated in his mind whether he should keep this place a secret for himself, or maybe tell his friend about it sometime. He'd think about it.

Billy took up a stance just outside Mooney's pub and held one of the Telegraphs across his chest so everyone could see it. That's the way Stumpy did it, and Stumpy knew everything there was to know about selling newspapers.

There was only one problem. The rain. His newspapers were getting wet and limp and the pages were beginning to stick together. He couldn't remember how Stumpy kept his papers dry from the rain. He gazed across the street at the warm lights of the Royal cinema and the black and white placards of Al Jolson outside. The citizens of Belfast, regardless of age, were big fans of the great stars of the silver screen. There were plenty of people streaming in to see Jolie singing in blackface. It would be warmer and drier over there on the picture house steps and maybe some of the people going in to see Jolson would buy his papers. That's what he would do. Move over to the picture house steps.

He never saw the punch coming. He didn't even know it was a punch. He just felt the tearing jagged pain as his lip was suddenly split open against his front teeth and he tasted the salty blood in his mouth as he reeled backwards. Another blow caught him high up on the temple and sent him crashing to the ground and his papers flying in the wind across the street.

As he lay on the ground Billy's hand went instinctively to his mouth when he tasted the blood. He stared in disbelief at the red gore on his fingers. Then he caught a glimpse of his Telegraphs lying scattered in the gutter. He jumped to his feet, mad with rage as he suddenly realized what had happened. He swung a wild punch at the big newsboy who stood over him, fists held high. The punch missed by a mile and the bigger boy smashed another sickening blow into Billy's face, sending him crashing to the ground for a second time. The big boy didn't give Billy time to recover. He grabbed him by the scruff of the jersey and hauled him to his feet, shaking him like a rag doll.

"Listen you," he snarled, his nose not half an inch from Billy's. "I don't want to hit you again. But if you set foot on my patch again I'll bust ye in two!" He pushed Billy roughly away from him. "Now clear off! And take yer papers with ye and get a pitch of yer own. If I see ye back here I'll hammer ye senseless!"

Billy spat out blood and glared at the bigger boy. He was no coward. But he was beaten. And he knew it. Even if he did swing another punch he knew he couldn't reach high enough to connect. The big newsboy, who still had his fists at the ready, would probably tear his Telegraphs into shreds. And he had to save his newspapers. Even more than his pride, he had to save the Telegraphs. Without the newspapers there would be no *The Book of One Thousand Beautiful Things*. He wiped the cuff of his jersey across his bleeding mouth and picked up his papers, ignoring the curses and abuse hurled at him by the big newsboy. The newspapers were wet. Very wet. Worse, they were torn and splattered with mud. He gathered them up one by one and dried and cleaned them as best he could. When he had them altogether in a rough bundle he shoved them under his arm. Then he trudged wearily down Arthur Street, trying to stem the blood flowing into his mouth. He didn't know where to go. Or what to do next.

Billy couldn't sell a single newspaper. Not one. He'd cleaned and dried and tidied them as best he could. It was all wasted effort. An unused newspaper has a freshness and crispness and a secret waiting to be uncovered. There may be thousands of copies of the same edition, but to its owner his newspaper is unique – unopened, untouched by any hand save his own – its hidden parts reserved for him alone. The mere expectation of the delights within its folds is a pleasure often deliberately delayed until they may be enjoyed at a convenient time when all attention can be devoted to the enjoyment of it, in comfort and ease and privacy. No one wanted a soiled newspaper tainted with the mud of the streets, torn and limp, abused and uncared for.

Billy was desperate. Now there were only a few stragglers about the gas-lit streets. Anyone who had wanted an evening paper had bought one long ago. He was in big trouble. It wasn't only that he hadn't been able to sell the newspapers to make up the other three pennies he needed. It was worse than that. All his hard earned cash, the entire six pennies, was tied up in the six worthless newspapers stuck under his arm. He was back where he started. With nothing. What was it his da' had said to him last night? He had ideas above his station? Something like that. He wasn't quite sure what that meant, but maybe it meant a kid like him would never be able to get enough money to buy *The Book of One Thousand Beautiful Things*. Maybe that's what it meant and that's why the big lad had punched him in the mouth and kicked his papers up into the air and into the gutter. Because he had ideas above his station.

Billy paused outside a pub in Chichester Street. Tenderly he drew a finger along his bruised lip. The bleeding had stopped and so had the rain and the bright light of the pub window cheered him. He listened to the raised voices and laughter coming from inside as the patrons cheered themselves from glass and bottle in an effort to make the best of what would be a hard Christmas for most of them. Billy fingered his newspapers slowly. He pursed his lips as an idea began to form in his mind. Maybe, just maybe, it might work. Maybe there was still a chance. Anyway, it was worth a try. Anything was worth a try.

Billy pushed open the door of the pub and squeezed inside. The bar was comfortable and even the tiled floor was warm to his feet. The air was heavy with tobacco smoke and noisy with conversation. Close by the door and near a blazing fire two old men stared solemnly at a draughtboard. Billy watched the men for a moment, interested to see what the next move in the game would be, and what would be the consequences of it. But neither man moved, nor gave any indication he was likely to and Billy lost interest as his gaze travelled around the bar.

The high wooden booths were well filled, mostly by men with bottles of Guinness and pint glasses in front of them. But there were women there too. They were old women, almost as old as the witch in Vistula Street, and they sipped slowly at tiny glasses of red wine and what Billy knew to be 'half-uns'.

The group of men who stood arguing at the bar were a rougher breed, probably dockers, and the big man with the ginger curls and red and green checked shirt seemed to be the roughest of the lot. Billy watched as the man banged his empty glass on the counter and demanded another 'bottle by the neck' for himself and his four friends. When he'd finished barking out his order Billy made his move.

"Telegraph? Anybody want a Telegraph?"

No one was listening. Not to him, not to each other. Everybody was talking, but no one was listening, each voice striving to rise higher than its fellows as it sought to make itself heard, just the way it was at home. Corks plunked as they were yanked from bottles by the fat little barman with the white shirt and black apron. Glasses chinked "here's to you", "good health", and "bottoms up" and the women laughed coarsely at some vulgar joke told by one of their number. The big man with the ginger curls demanded service at once and threatened to take his custom and that of his four companions over to Mooney's if his order wasn't immediately attended to.

Only the draughts players seemed aloof from it all. Billy's eyes travelled back to the two men who sat unblinking and unmoving. Suddenly one of the men did move, lifting his right hand and holding it about an eighth of an inch above his red crowner. The man held his hand quite motionless in this position for almost half a minute as Billy moved forward, excited to see the move and what the effects of it would be.

But there wasn't any move. Billy watched in disappointment as the man shook his head and slowly lowered his hand back to the glass-topped table and brought his other hand up to stroke a worried brow. Billy moved closer.

"Telegraph, mister? Do you want to buy a Tele?"

The man shook his head and waved the back of his hand without even looking up. "Go away, son. Go away. I'm in trouble. Big trouble."

Billy nodded and turned away. Maybe he'd try the big man with the ginger hair. The man was noisy and demonstrative, but in a good-hearted way, a happy drunk. Happy drunks could sometimes be generous drunks, free with their pennies.

Billy tugged at the big man's sleeve. "Do you want to buy a Telegraph, mister?"

The man stopped halfway through a bout of raucous laughter and looked down at Billy. He banged his pint glass on the counter and suddenly brought his face right down level with Billy's so he was staring him right in the eye.

"Do I want to buy WHAT?" he roared.

Billy jerked his head back quickly from the big man's face, not in fear, for drunk men held no terrors for him, but in order to escape the sickly beery smell of the man's breath.

"A Telegraph, mister. Do you want to buy a Telegraph?"

The man threw his head back and laughed loudly, his face taking on the same colour as his red neckerchief and causing Billy to believe the man had taken a fit. But just as suddenly, he stopped laughing.

"Naw!" he bellowed. "We don't want no Telegraphs! Do we boys?"

The boys, not one of them a day under fifty, shook their heads dolefully in unanimous agreement with their leader.

"We don't want no papers," bawled the big man as he nipped Billy's cheek with two rough fingers. "What would we want with Telegraphs! It's a song we want. Isn't it, boys? Now, if you were able to sing a song - well, ye might be able to sell a paper or two. But if ye can't sing ye won't sell no papers."

Billy stared hard into the big man's eyes, trying to see into his mind. If he sang a song, would the big man really buy a paper? Or was he just using him to get a laugh?

"Well?" demanded the big man. He wasn't laughing now. His face was deadly serious. "Can ye sing?"

Billy completed his assessment of the big man. He nodded slowly. "I can sing, mister. What do you want to hear?"

The man grabbed Billy by the scruff of the neck and yanked him up on top of the bar. "Anything! Sing whatever ye want, and we'll all buy a paper. Won't we boys?"

The boys raised their glasses in confirmation of their leader's declaration of intent and stared expectantly at Billy. Billy straightened his papers beside him on the bar and nervously cleared his throat.

When Billy began to sing *I'll Take You Home Again Kathleen* he simply could not be heard above the laughter and the shouting and the clinking of glasses and the popping of corks. Then, little by little, the laughter slowly died away and the shouting lowered and there wasn't any clinking of glasses and the plunking of corks from bottles ceased. Finally there wasn't a sound to be heard in the entire bar save the clear bell-like tones of an unbroken voice hitting and holding every note with perfect ease and clarity.

When Billy finished singing there was a strange silence, a silence you don't often get in pubs except when they're bolted and locked up for the night. He sat uncomfortably on the bar, embarrassed that every face and every gaze was fixed on him. He was about to explain he could have sung the song better if he didn't have a sore lip when the whole place erupted in a cacophony of sound – applause, whistles, cheers, demands to "do another one" and advice that he should be "on at the Empire." Billy stared into the sea of cheering faces, not quite comprehending all the good wishes and compliments which were directed toward him. He jumped down from the bar beaming from ear to ear and forgetting all about the Telegraphs and *The Book of One Thousand Beautiful Things*. He bowed three times as the big docker took out a dirty handkerchief and blew his nose with great vigour, taking the opportunity to wipe away whatever it was that was escaping from his eyes. The big man stuck the handkerchief back in his pocket and tousled Billy's hair in a friendly fashion.

"Son, that was great!" he sniffed, giving his eyes another rub with his knuckles. "Great! I niver heard Kathleen sung like that in all m'days. Niver. Ye hit them notes as true as amber. Ye did, son. As true as amber!"

Billy basked modestly amidst the praise showered upon him from all directions, trying at the same time to understand what the big man meant by "true as amber". He declined the offer of a "half-un" to do another song but quickly downed the tumbler of brown lemonade set up for him by the enthusiastic barman. When he finished it he picked his cap from the floor and stuck it on his head. Then he remembered why he was there. He looked meaningfully at the newspapers on the counter.

The big docker laughed loudly and grabbed the Telegraphs. He held them away from him at arms length as if they were so much dead fish.

"How much are ye lukkin' for these?"

Billy took a deep breath. "Ninepence, mister. For the whole lot!"

"Ninepence!" The big man laughed derisively and flung the newspapers back on the counter. "Ninepence! I wuddn't give ye tuppence for them!"

The elation of a moment ago departed from Billy suddenly and completely to be replaced with a heavy sinking feeling in the pit of his stomach. Then his eyes opened wide in astonishment as the big man put his hand into a pocket and pulled out a sixpenny piece and a thruppenny bit.

"I wouldn't give ye tuppence for them," he laughed. "Not if I wanted to read them. But Pat M'Clusky's word is Pat M'Clusky's bond. There's yer ninepence, and there's yer papers as well. Ye're a brave wee singer, and ye might make yer name at it. But I don't think newspaper-sellin' is the game for you. Ye couldn't give them papers away. Ye couldn't' even light the fire with them."

Billy grinned. He picked up his money and lifted his newspapers and thanked the big man over and over again. He bowed one last time to his appreciative audience and promised to come back and sing for them again, finally leaving the pub to another round of applause and cheers and whistles.

Billy pulled the door closed behind him and took a deep breath of the cold night air. The rain had stopped. A pale moon hung in a cold starry sky, reminding him of the shiny silver sixpence in his pocket. He reckoned the sixpence was just about the same size as the moon and every bit as shiny. He extracted the coin from his pocket and held it up to the sky between his finger and thumb. The sixpence was indeed exactly the same size as the moon and blotted it from the sky. But the light shining from the window behind him struck his silver sixpence making it gleam, a silvery gleam, just like the moon.

Billy shoved the newspapers into a rubbish bin at the side of the pub. He stuck his hands into the warmth of his trouser pockets. He smiled, and winked at the moon. Tomorrow was Christmas Eve. It would be a great day.

Christmas Eve morning was bright. The red mackerel sky moving slowly across the city from the direction of the shipyard gantries did nothing to take the nip from the air. But it was early yet.

Billy stopped at the corner of Smithfield Square and waited for O'Hara's breadcart to pass. The horse trotted easily with its full load and the brass harness gleamed brightly in the cold morning sun. The amalgamated smells of horse-sweat and leather and freshly baked bread and horse-manure hung in the air. Billy was still trying to track each smell to its source when a throb of wings above him made him look up.

A flock of pigeons swooped low over the Smithfield Square on their way to the grain mills at the edge of the docks. There was always plenty of spillage at the feed mills; corn, oats, wheat and barley. A lot of people in Belfast weren't eating too well this Christmas. But there was no need for a pigeon to go hungry. Billy watched the birds arc away across the Square. How did they all know to change direction at the same time? And how could they do it so quickly and without crashing into each other? Pigeons were clever. Frankie M'Conkey, who was one class ahead of him in school, said you could take a pigeon to Bangor, in a box, and let it go and it would fly right back where it came from. Even in the dark. Billy didn't believe it. But Frankie said it was true, and he didn't think Frankie told lies. Maybe there'd be something about pigeons in *The Book of One Thousand Beautiful Things*. But he didn't mind if there wasn't. There'd be hundreds of other things to read and look at in the book. He could hardly wait to get it.

Billy lifted a hand and shaded his eyes against the glare of the bright sun as he watched the pigeons disappear over Chapel Lane. He stepped off the footpath and strode into the market, a cheery grin on his face. In a few minutes *The Book of One Thousand Beautiful Things* would be his. It would belong to him and he could read it from cover to cover, over and over again, as many times as he wished. And he would print his name on the very first page so everyone would know this was Billy McCullough's book.

The old man with the grinding wheel was already labouring to set up his contraption at the Gresham Street end of the market as Billy came in. Francie's pet rabbits – Francie said they were special rabbits – Dutch, from Holland, black and white, with twitching pink noses – were being lined up in their cages outside the front of the shop. Goldfish swam round and round in their tiny bowls high up on top of the rabbit hutches, well out of reach of grasping little hands.

Billy stuck his tongue out at the brilliantly coloured parrot above the doorway and laughed as it cursed him with a flurry of feathers and ruffling wings. Then, triumphantly, he turned the door handle and walked into Barney's Smithfield Secondhand Bookshop.

The task of threading a path across the book-covered floor was no easier than it had been on his first visit. But he managed it without touching any of the volumes with his bare feet. When he reached the counter he gazed over the pile of old books and newspapers and magazines which seemed to have grown even higher than they were before. Even on tiptoes he could just about see the little man behind the counter. When Billy spoke there was a note of quiet pride in his voice.

"I got it, mister. I got the money. For the book."

Barney looked up from the Zane Grey in which he was already well engrossed despite the earliness of the day. He rubbed the sleep from his eyes. He'd been at a wake the night before. The crack had been mighty, and the whiskey even better. But now he was feeling the worse for it and he wondered if a hair of the dog that bit him mightn't set him up for the day. His little racing eyes squinted at Billy in a puzzled frown.

"What book was that, son?"

Billy smiled, pleased the man was asking him to say the name of the book out loud.

"*The Book of One Thousand Beautiful Things*. The blue one. With Ye Banks and Braes O' Bonny Doon in it."

Barney pulled the pencil-stub from behind his ear and carefully marked the place in his Zane Grey. He stuck the pencil back on his ear. Wearily, he rose from his stool. He yawned.

"Oh. That book. A fella was in here yesterday. Real toff. Silk scarf and everything. Offered me one and thruppence for it. Said he'd been lookin' for it for years."

The smile left Billy's face instantly and totally. What did the man say? Did he say he'd sold *The Book of One Thousand Beautiful Things*? His book? To somebody else? He tried to speak. But the words wouldn't come out and a big lump which he thought was going to choke him rose in his throat. He felt his lower lip tremble and he was afraid he was going to cry. He hadn't cried when the big lad in Corn Market had thumped him in the mouth and split it open and kicked his papers into the gutter. He hadn't cried then. But he was afraid he was going to cry now.

Billy stared helplessly at the man, trying to make sense of what he had just heard. But it didn't make sense and all he wanted to do was run. Run as fast as he could from Barney's Smithfield Secondhand Bookshop, run and never ever come back. It didn't matter now that he would never own *The Book of One Thousand Beautiful Things*. His da' had been right. He had ideas above his station. *The Book of One Thousand Beautiful Things* would never be his and no other book would ever be his because he never wanted to see another book as long as he lived. And he'd never, ever, trust anybody again.

But Billy held out a shaking palm to reveal the sixpence and the thruppenny bit in a final gesture of proof that he hadn't gone back on his word. He'd kept his part of the bargain.

"But I got the money, mister. I gathered refuse and broke sticks and sold Teles. I got the money." Then his head went down and his lip trembled and he couldn't hold back the tears and he turned away so the man wouldn't see. He was hurt and confused and as he picked his way back to the door he determined no one would ever hurt him again. He ignored Barney's pleas to come back. He was almost out the door when he felt Barney's touch at his elbow and his arm around his shoulder. He stiffened and pulled away from whatever grain of comfort the man was trying to offer. But Barney gently turned him around and pointed to the corner.

"Listen, son. Away over to that box sittin' at the end of the counter. Take a look inside it." Barney's voice was low and apologetic and a little embarrassed. He squeezed Billy's arm gently. "Go on, son. Look in the box."

Billy wiped his sleeve across his face. He turned slowly and allowed himself to be led back to the counter. Barney pointed to the box.

"Go on, son. That box. Put your hand in."

Billy reached into the box. His hand closed on something - a book - and when he pulled it out he knew, he just knew, without opening it, it was *The Book of One Thousand Beautiful Things*. But he did open it, just to be sure – and yes – they were all there – the poems, the paintings, the verses from the Bible and the wise sayings of wise men who lived long, long ago. Now Billy's tears were gone, the sadness and despair of a moment replaced with joy and happiness and a great big smile, his blue eyes shining.

"You did keep it for me, mister," he shouted excitedly. "You did! You kept it for me!" A puzzled expression drifted over his shining face. "But you told me you sold it, mister. Why did you tell me you sold it to the man?"

Barney grinned, glad he had resisted the temptation to let the book go. Times were tough and the offer had been tempting, and he might never have seen the kid again, or the ninepence he'd been trying to scrape up. But it was worth dropping the tanner just to see the happiness on the kid's face.

"I didn't say I sold it. I said a fella offered me one and thruppence for it. But I didn't say I'd sold it. Did you think I'd sell it? After you and me had made a deal on it?"

Now it was Billy's turn to be embarrassed. He blushed and pushed the coins, the sixpence and the thruppenny bit, toward Barney, glad to be rid of them so he could use both hands to skim through the pages of the book once more. He stopped at a picture of The Angelus. What did this mean? Why were these two poor people standing in this field? Were they praying? What story lay behind this picture? Barney made a move to pick up the ninepence. He hesitated as a thought, which he tried to quickly dismiss, shot into his mind. Was he going crackers? Or was he just getting soft in his old age? If he didn't catch himself on he'd be out of business in next to no time. Aw, to heck with it. He pushed the coins back toward Billy. "I don't want no money, son. Take the book. Take it away with you."

Billy's mouth dropped open. "For nothin', mister? Do you mean you're givin' it to me? For nothin?" Barney sniffed. He wasn't used to this sort of situation and he wasn't comfortable in it. Business was business and he usually extracted the last farthing from his customers, rich or poor. He couldn't understand his action, never mind explain it. But he did his best. "I've no family of my own, son. Nobody to give a present to. So let's just say it's a wee Christmas Box. From me to you."

"Aw thanks mister! Thanks a million!" exclaimed Billy, jumping up and down with excitement. He paused. "Mister! When I'm rich, I'll buy all my books from you. I will mister. Honest!" He paused again and looked earnestly at Barney. "Mister! Maybe someday I'll write books of my own and you could sell them in your shop. That would be good. Wouldn't it, mister?"

Barney sniffed. He gazed at the skinny bare-footed kid who'd probably be turfed out to work, if any work could be found for him, at thirteen or fourteen. He drew a rag from his pocket and blew his nose. "That – that would be great kid. You could write books of your own. That would be great, kid." He picked up a small battered volume from the floor and thrust it into Billy's hands. "Take that away with you, son. It's a dictionary. Maybe it'll tell you what a brae is. And it'll tell you the meanin' of every word in the English language. A wee Christmas Box. From me to you."

Billy grasped the small book. "Aw thanks mister! Thanks a million!" Billy clutched his treasures to his heart and headed toward the door. He laid his hand on the door handle. He turned his head and gazed earnestly at Barney. "I'll come back again. I will mister. Honest. But Happy Christmas to you mister. And many of them!"

Barney nodded and sniffed again. He stuck the rag back in his pocket and watched Billy push his way out into the snow which was beginning to fall on Gresham Street. The kid was a dreamer. Probably couldn't even read the books he protected so carefully from the snow and sleet and now he was talking about writing books of his own. The world was a hard place for dreamers. He knew. He'd been a dreamer. Once. Believed in Christmas too. Just like the kid. But that was long ago and far away, before the cares of the world had got to him. Maybe the kid would have better luck. He hoped so.

Barney shuffled over to the door. He pulled it open and felt the bitter cold as he watched Billy disappear into the snowy whiteness of a Christmas card Christmas Eve. He gazed after the youngster. Remembering. Just remembering. He raised a hand and waved. "Thanks, kid," he murmured. "Thanks a million. And a Happy Christmas to you kid. And many of them." He closed the door gently and shuffled back to his stool behind the counter, fumbling in his pocket for the remains of a Woodbine. He lit up and opened his Zane Grey, running his finger over the lines of print until he found the pencil mark he'd made when Billy had come into the shop. He leaned back on his stool and blew two circles of smoke to the ceiling. He watched the circles until they disappeared. When they did he lowered his head, and began to read.

Barney Magee, proprietor of Barney's Smithfield Secondhand Bookshop, didn't sell many books that Christmas in hungry nineteen-thirties Belfast. But the two he gave away brought him a friendship and richness in heart far beyond that which money could ever buy. The two books were the only Christmas presents Billy received. But they created in him a great love for the beauty of the written word and many years later he did indeed go on to write stories and books of his own. And all his books, and all his writings, reflected something of the truth and beauty and goodness and love he had found, within the pages, of *The Book of One Thousand Beautiful Things*.

The Return of Brian Boru

Dan O'Doherty sat on the river bank. He was at peace with the world and minding his own business when he first saw the leprechaun. There it was – on as nice a summer day as you could wish to see, rowing up the river toward him in a little grass-green boat which perfectly matched the tiny figure's loose-fitting cloak and pointed hat with a tiny gold bell at the top. The little bell tinkled sweetly each time the leprechaun leaned forward and pulled at the oars.

Dan blinked. He didn't believe in leprechauns. He'd never seen a leprechaun before, let alone one that had his own boat and could row it no bother at all. Dan laid his fishing-rod down quietly in the long warm grass and took a long, long look at the figure rowing toward him. He stared unbelievingly as the boat and the jaunty character who pulled effortlessly at the oars came closer and closer. Finally, when the boat was almost directly opposite Dan, the leprechaun rested the oars and called out, directly to him.

"Ahoy there Dan! Sparkling morning! Doing a spot of fishing I see. Lovely day for it. Mind if I join you for a bit? I could do with a rest!"

Dan's jaw dropped even lower as he heard the leprechaun call him by name. "N-n-no. I-I mean yes - yes. If you want to. I don't mind."

"That's dacent of you," chortled the leprechaun as he glided the boat into the river bank among the soft grasses and rushes. He sprung out from the little craft, as light on his tiny feet as a hen's feather on a summer breeze. "That's one magical day, Dan," he enthused, throwing himself down on the bank beside the bewildered fisherman, the little bell in his cap tinkling all the while. "One magical day!"

It was indeed a magical day. Just about the most magical day Dan had ever witnessed, what with a leprechaun who rowed a boat and knew his name into the bargain, and who could talk as good as any Irishman he'd ever come across.

"How is it you'd be knowin' my name?" demanded Dan, eyeing the elfin figure suspiciously. "I don't think I ever met ye before?"

The leprechaun sat up and leaned his back into the stump of a tree-trunk. He crossed his thin legs and clasped his hands behind his head, basking in the warm overhead sun.

"I know everyone's name," he beamed, "and everything about them. Everyone. From here to Cork and Kerry, and even up the North to Derry." He paused. "Begorrah! Isn't that musical! From here to Cork and Kerry, and even up the North to Derry! What talent! Oh! What delight! It's wonderful to be a leprechaun! I could wish for no better life!"

Dan stared hard at the figure in green, his bushy eyebrows knitting into a deep frown. He pointed a finger at the leprechaun. "I've never seen you around here before. Where do you come from?"

The leprechaun sat bolt upright, the bell in his pixie cap tinkling loudly as he turned to face Dan. "Where do I come from!"

he reiterated. "Where do I come from! Well! Of all the nerve! I've ALWAYS been here! It's only in the past fifty or sixty years I've seen you come about the place. Where did I come from! Humph! Interlopers!"

"I - I didn't mean to offer any offence," stuttered Dan, drawing back a little from the leprechaun. "It's just that I've never seen you before. I thought you were a stranger here."

"Well I'm not," huffed the leprechaun. Then, smiling broadly he snuggled back into the comfort of the tree-trunk, again clasping his hands behind his head. "But, I'll say no more about it. Tell me though, what brought you to these parts?"

Dan considered remaining silent on the grounds the leprechaun had already stated he knew everything about everyone. Then he remembered the shortness and quickness of the leprechaun's temper.

"Me mother and me father brought me. From Kinsale. When I was three months old," Dan grunted, as conciliatory as possible.

The leprechaun pulled a shoot of young grass and chewed on it, enjoying the sweetness. He nodded his head. "Ah yes," he mused. "I recall something of that. It wasn't so very long ago."

Dan sniffed. Sixty-two years wasn't exactly yesterday. But he wasn't going to argue, deciding instead to humour his new-found companion.

"I didn't expect to see a leprechaun rowing up the river in broad daylight," chuckled Dan as he pulled himself a shoot of grass to accompany the leprechaun. "I thought you all lived in a hawthorn bush."

"Bah!" snorted the leprechaun pushing his tiny face to within an inch of Dan's nose. "Did you ever see a leprechaun in a hawthorn bush? Did you? Ever? What would a leprechaun be doing in a prickly hawthorn bush! What would ANYONE, with any sense, be doing in a hawthorn bush? The very thought of it! Bah! What nonsense!"

Dan shut his mouth, tightly, and resolved not to open it again. He didn't know as much about leprechauns as he'd thought he did. Maybe if he said nothing this one would go away and he could get back to fishing in peace.

But the leprechaun didn't go away. The mischievous grin spread over the leprechaun's cheeky face once more as he punched Dan playfully in the midriff, knocking the wind from him. "Dan, my dear fellow! You haven't asked my name! Wouldn't you like to know my name?"

Now it was Dan's turn to huff. He couldn't care less what the leprechaun's name was. Mickeleen. Barney. Seamus. Darby O'Gill. It was all one to him. But he couldn't afford to offend the little fellow who packed such a mighty punch for one so tiny. Dan stroked his white stubble and forced a little smile.

"Sure isn't that just what I've been wonderin' the whole time since I met you," he cackled. "Tell me now. What IS your name?"

"Well! I am delighted you asked," enthused the leprechaun as he bounded to his feet. "Absolutely delighted!" He made a sweeping bow in front of Dan and the little bell on his hat tinkled. "You have the great honour, my dear fellow, to see before you, the one - the only - Brian Boru!"

Dan swallowed hard. "Brian - Brian Boru! I don't suppose you'd be any relation to the Brian Boru that was king of all Ireland?"

"Relation!" screeched the leprechaun, waving his arms in the air and dancing a jig of fiery temper on the green sward beneath his tiny feet. "Relation! Sir! I am no relation! I AM that important personage. I am he!"

Dan, fearing another blow to the solar plexus, this time of a more vindictive nature was about to come his way, decided to put matters right immediately. "Ah, yes, yes," he replied hastily. "I thought I recognized the likeness. But didn't you get killed at Clontarf? About a thousand years ago?"

Well, if Dan thought he was pouring oil on troubled waters he very quickly discovered he was attempting to put out a blazing furnace by dousing it with as much high-octane fuel as he could lay his hands on. The leprechaun commenced a dance of absolutely frenzied proportions, his face turning purple with rage as he stamped his feet on the ground and did two or three complete somersaults for good measure.

"Killed!" shrieked the leprechaun. "Killed! If I had been killed how is it I'm standing in front of you now! Lies! Lies! Lies! All put about by the enemies of the great King Brian – lies that have now entered into the history books as facts! Oh that the great King Brian should be so used and misrepresented!"

King Brian threw himself on the ground, pounding the soft earth with his tiny fists and sobbing quietly while Dan bit his lip and considered making a run for it. Fearful this would enrage King Brian even more, resulting in dear knows what terrible consequences, he restrained his natural impulse. He stretched out a hand and laid it on King Brian's little head.

"There now," he murmured comfortingly. "Don't be takin' on so, yer Majesty. Sure doesn't the whole population of Ireland believe you'll be comin' back any day to lead us once again. And sure you're world famous already. And didn't I hear just the other day they're thinkin' about erectin' a statue of yerself in Dublin. Now. Won't that be just grand? When that happens? Won't it now?"

King Brian's sobbing became more and more stifled until it ceased completely. He turned his head on the grass and peered at Dan with one eye. "A monument? To me? In Dublin's fair city? Well! That certainly has brightened my day, Dan. A monument to me! In Dublin! How wonderful!"

King Brian sprang to his feet then threw himself down again against the tree-stump. He picked up Dan's fishing-rod and flicked it lazily over the gently flowing river. "Catch anything today, Dan?"

Dan pulled another shoot of grass and stroked his chin with it. "Ach, not a thing. Not even a bite. And me tryin' to win the prize for the biggest fish ever to be caught in this river. The one to beat is still above the bar in Marty Madonnell's pub. It's been there forty years. And it'll probably be there for another forty. You've probably seen it." Dan hesitated. "Then again, maybe ye haven't. But that's how long I've been tryin' to win the record. Forty long years."

"You're fishing in the wrong part of the river, Dan."

Dan stared at King Brian. "I'm what?"

"You heard me. You're fishing in the wrong part of the river."

Now it was Dan's turn to be peeved. What did a leprechaun, even if he was a King, know about fishing? Maybe he had won battles glorious, slayed his thousands and tens of thousands. But, to the best of his knowledge – and he knew a fair bit about fishing – there was no record of King Brian Boru winning any angling competitions.

"Ah now yer Majesty," smiled Dan, not wishing to put the leprechaun out of humour, "it's true I'm not havin' much luck today. But I've been fishin' this river for more years than I can remember. I've seen fish nearly two feet long at this very spot."

"Stickle-backs" retorted King Brian. "Small fry. Spricks. I know where the real fish are – some of them born even before I came to the throne. Including one you'll hardly get through the door of Marty's pub. If you were lucky enough to catch it."

Now, if Dan had taken the happenings of the morning with the proverbial grain of salt, totally convinced the leprechaun was completely off his tiny rocker, he now paid full heed at the mention of fish. Big fish. How old did King Brian say they were?

"Yer Majesty – King Brian," spluttered Dan, "whereabouts do ye think this fish might be?"

"Think?" repeated King Brian. "My dear fellow! I do not think. I know. And I'll show you where to catch it. On condition my name goes on the winner's plaque beside yours, to allay the vile rumours I am no longer alive. Is it a deal?"

It was a deal. "Right," exclaimed King Brian, bounding to his feet. "Into my boat and off we go!"

Dan and King Brian Boru the leprechaun rowed by day and rowed by yellow moonlight. They rowed for six days and six nights until Dan had no idea if they were still in Ireland or out of it, or whether they were well on their way to America, and he might never see home again. It was near to another midnight when bats squeaked and owls hooted in the dark trees when King Brian finally let the boat glide gently alongside the long grasses and rushes of the river bank and bounded out. "Right Dan," he chirped. "Out you come now. Get your line ready."

"What for?" protested Dan, who hadn't slept in almost a week and was looking forward to a good night's kip. "You can't catch fish at this time of night. Not where I come from."

"Ah, but this isn't where you come from," laughed King Brian mischievously. "This is a very different place. Come on now! Cast off. You've got about two minutes to do it. Before midnight. Or you've lost your chance of landing the biggest fish in all Ireland. Forever!"

Dan's fly had barely hit the moonlit water when his fishing rod bent double and Dan was hauled into the river nearly up to his neck before he could say Darby O'Gill and The Little People.

"Ah you've got him Dan! You've got him! " screamed King Brian, marking the occasion with six complete somersaults and tossing in a verse from *Phil the Fluters Ball* for good measure.

"Well come in and help me!" spluttered Dan, spouting out a mouthful of water. "I'll never be able to land this one on my own! It's a monster! A monster!"

"Ah now Dan," laughed King Brian. "I know it's a monster! Isn't that what you wanted! But I've done all I promised. The rest is up to you!" Then, without as much as by your leave, he jumped into his little boat and began to pull away down the river.

"Ach now, don't be leavin' me Brian, yer Majesty," pleaded Dan between mouthfuls of water as he went under for the third time, still clinging desperately to the arching rod. "Sure I don't even know where I am. And I haven't got a boat. I'll never get home again, even supposin' I don't drown right here!"

"You're nearer home than you think, Dan," chortled the leprechaun. "With the biggest fish in all Ireland for company! Have a pleasant evening! But don't be forgetting your promise to King Brian! Goodbye, Dan! Goodbye!"

Now, I could fill up another page or two telling you all about how Dan struggled all the night long to land the biggest fish in Ireland, and how it took Micky Donnegan's donkey and cart and a dozen men to haul it to the village and how when the sun came over the mountain in the morning Dan was at the same place on the river as he was when he first spotted King Brian Boru. But what difference would that make? You either believe the whole story or you think it's a duncherful of Irish blarney. But if you don't believe it, and you don't believe in the little people, you could do worse than take a wee dander down to Marty Madonnell's pub the next time you're in the area. Take a good look at the big fish running the length of the whole reinforced wall behind the bar. Marty himself will tell you how the fish came to be there. Or ask the locals. And if you don't believe them, the facts are plainly stated on the solid brass plaque beneath the big fish.

LEVIATHAN !
The biggest fish in all Ireland.
Landed (we think) in the parish of Killybane by Mr Dan O'Doherty,
ably assisted by His Royal Majesty Brian Boru, King of all Ireland !

Dan O'Doherty believes in leprechauns. And most evenings you'll see him down on the river bank, waiting patiently. For the return of Brian Boru.

Just a Poor Bachelor

She wasn't coming. I knew she wasn't coming. I'd been long enough at this game to know what was what. If she'd been coming she'd have been here by now – and I wouldn't be hanging about like Gene Kelly – but without the umbrella and without the music, and shivering as the icy rain dripped down the back of my neck.

It was a woman's prerogative to be late. I knew that. It was all part of the game. Just the way it is at weddings. The bride driving round the block half a dozen times, on purpose, as if she couldn't quite decide whether to commit the rest of her life to her beloved, or not to bother, and keeping the poor fella waiting at the altar, an absolute bundle of nerves. It was all part of the game.

But twenty-five minutes? On a winter's night like this with a gale force wind howling up High Street from Portaferry and emptying the half of Strangford Lough right on top of me at the corner of Conway Square? There should be a law against it. Equal rights for men. Something like that.

A car splashed by, momentarily brightening up the dimly lit street with a wet blaze of yellow headlights which showed me just how hard the rain was lashing down. I stared after the car as it splashed away up Mill Street. That's what you needed now to get anywhere with the birds. A car. They didn't keep you hanging about if you had a motor car. All I had was the pushbike leaning against the lamp post across the street.

I shivered and pulled up my collar, trying to get a bit of protection from the rain and biting wind. Then, more in desperation than expectation, I poked my head out from the shop doorway. The street was deserted. The town hall clock said twenty-six minutes past seven. She was supposed to be here at seven. She wouldn't come now. Too late.

I turned my head in the other direction. You never could tell. Women were unpredictable. They were renowned for it. You just couldn't depend on them to do the right thing. She might be coming the other way.

She wasn't. Nothing. Only the warm red and yellow dazzle of a fish and chip shop neon flickering on and off against the sheets of rain. It would take more than fish and chips to drag anybody with an ounce of sense out on a night like this. But I could make a big hole in a well salted and vinegared fish supper if I had it set up to me right now. I watched the hard spikes of rain shaft past the lonely street lamp and bounce angrily off the streaming footpath.

I sighed, a big deep sigh, and stepped farther back into the doorway. I'd give her another ten minutes. Ten minutes more than she was worth. I fumbled for a cigarette. You're never alone with a feg, I thought to myself. I'll light a feg. I couldn't get it lit. The rain and the wind snuffed out the match every time, as soon it flared into life. Humphrey Bogart never had this trouble, whatever the weather, I thought to myself as I got down to my last match. This time I made it. Just about. I took a puff and blew a circle of smoke out into the wind. The wind blew it straight back in my face.

But that was the trouble with women. You couldn't depend on them. They weren't rational. And you couldn't believe a word they said. If they told you straight they didn't want to go out with you you'd know exactly where you were. In the h'penny place. It dented your pride, and mine had been dented fairly often. But at least it didn't waste your time.

Then there was the sort who led you on with flashing smiles and half glances from under dark eyelashes, making you believe you were the ultimate object of every women's desire, and about ten feet tall into the bargain. It was great for the 'oul ego. Then, when you finally get rid of the dryness in your throat and pluck up the courage to ask her out she's afraid she couldn't manage that particular night.

What about the next night? She was washing her hair. Women were always washing their hair. Some sort of nervous habit. Could she not wash it on another night? No. She always washed it on Tuesday nights. How about Saturday then? That would give her plenty of time to get the hair washed. And dried as well. Would Saturday be okay?

No. She had to go to her granny's birthday party on Saturday. You thought about indicating you would be quite happy – if it would get her out of a tough spot – to accompany her to the old girl's soiree. Then you remembered you'd never actually been introduced to grandma. So, that was out. But you wanted to be as accommodating as you could. Would my wild Irish rose care to pick a night of her own choosing?

Well, she'd love to. She would. Really. Nothing would give her more pleasure. It was just that she was so terribly busy at the present time and didn't have a night free between this and Halloween. As this was a couple of days before Easter, you finally got the message.

That was bad enough, but then there was this one. The one who was keeping me hanging about in the rain like the proverbial drowned rat. Nice looking. Not glamorous. Pretty ordinary you might say. Not the flirty type. Probably not enough admirers for that. But a decent looking girl. No airs or graces and looking just as out of place at the party as I was. But we got on well together, just talking, in a quiet corner of the room while the rest of them did their thing. She was my type.

So I asked her out. Let me think about it, she says. I'll let you know when the party's over. Well, that's fair enough. No problem. She'll either say yes, or she'll say no. And I'll know exactly where I am.

So I don't rush her. I give her a bit of time and she says yes and now here I am hanging about like an advertisement for one of them Bachelor's Warm 'em up Soups and all because she hasn't got the guts to say no thank you.

To pot with them all. No point standing about here freezing. Still, there's time to catch the second half of the International on the box. International? Hold on a minute. That was last night. Nor'n Irelan' got beat again. Six to nothing. I'm a day late. I should have met her yesterday. Aw to heck with it. She probably didn't turn up anyway.

A Wee Night Out

Big Andy tossed his trowel into a bucket of water. He removed his peaked cap and wiped his bald head with a blue spotted handkerchief. He sighed and set his ample frame down on a half empty bag of cement. The building trade was getting tougher. It wasn't the same fun now – not the way it used to be. The crack was mighty when R. J. McKee & Son had been a family firm. Two or three joiners, a couple of brickies, Jimmy, the apprentice joiner, Woodbine the labourer, and himself, jack-of-all trades. It was good then. A bit of an extension to some wee house in Comber or maybe the renovation of a tumbledown shack in Conlig. A couple of months at the most on one job. Then, up with the trowel and the float and the hammer and away to pastures new. It was no fun now. Not since R. J. McKee had been gobbled up by the biggest building organization in the whole country. It wasn't the same being just one of a hundred tradesmen, most of whom you didn't know, building a brand new office block in the middle of Belfast. You weren't a name on the payroll now. You were a number. Just a number. And Andy didn't like his number. Fifty-three. Every time he collected his pay-packet on a Friday night the number stared him straight in the eye, mocking him. He wondered if somebody had found out about his age and deliberately used it as his payroll number. It wasn't a very nice thing to do. Big Andy had worked for R. J. McKee & Son – before it had been taken over – for almost twenty years. He still regarded R. J. McKee as his personal employer, even although R. J. had taken the money and run to spend his twilight years in a small mansion somewhere about leafy Cultra. Andy never got to visit him now. But for twenty years Andy had built walls for R. J. McKee. Built walls, plastered walls, knocked walls down, and built walls up again. For R. J. McKee, until he himself had come to be reckoned one of the permanent fixtures in the company, a man who couldn't be done without. Now he was just a number. Number fifty three. And he owed his job to the special behest of R. J. The new employers had wanted to get rid of Big Andy when they took the company over. Younger men were best.

Andy pulled a pipe from his overall pocket. He filled it with a few shreds of St. Bruno and packed it well into the bowl. He struck a match on the sole of his boot and held the flame to the tobacco, all the while looking thoughtfully over at Jimmy. The apprentice was fitting a mortice lock into a panelled door. Jimmy seemed happy enough at what he was doing. A right wee lad. Lived out in the country on a wee bit of a farm. Andy was also a farmer, or at least laid claim to that title. At one time he and his wife Bertha and the two sons had lived in a wooden lamp-lit bungalow on a couple of acres of stoney ground on the outskirts of Bangor. The ground was so rough and lifeless Andy couldn't get a scallion to grow on it. But it was okay for the couple of sows, a goat, and two or three Rhode Island Reds. And the two ducks. Andy liked a duck egg for his breakfast. With plenty of salt and a couple of rounds of well-buttered soda bread to dip into the yoke.

Big Andy had also owned, apart from the pigsty, a rusty, red

Nissen hut. It housed the goat and the hens and the ducks. It was slowly falling to bits, just like the bungalow. Like most men employed in the building trade, Big Andy took no pleasure in maintaining his own property. Not even the bungalow, let alone the Nissen hut. Many a winter night Andy sat by the fireside, turning a bit of turf and toasting his toes and debating with himself whether or not it might be a good decision to move himself and the family into the Nissen hut and let the goat and the hens and ducks take possession of the bungalow. Such was the similarity between the two buildings.

The nagging problem which had given Andy many a restless night in front of the fire was suddenly resolved when the local council decided to build a new ring road around Bangor town. The Council kindly informed Andy the intended road would run smack bang through his bungalow, entering by the front door and obligingly leaving by the back, and that the outside speed lane would be laid exactly where his Nissen hut now stood.

Big Andy, though not a man of great intellectual qualities, had enough sense to realize all this disruption would cause not inconsiderable inconvenience in the day to day running of his household, a point the Council readily conceded and proceeded to talk money so Andy and Bertha and family and associated livestock could move to a new home.

The Council decided five thousand pounds would be a reasonable sum, a lot of money in the late nineteen-fifties. Big Andy agreed this amount would cover his removal expenses admirably and now what about a figure for the purchase of a new home? Upon learning the cash the council offered was a once and for all figure for Big Andy and family and the goat and other friends to quit the site, Andy threatened to take the Council to the highest court in the land. They told him to go ahead. He did. The Council pleaded Andy's bungalow wasn't fit for human habitation and they were just about to put a demolition order on it and that it was only memory that was holding the Nissen hut up from the ground. The court decided otherwise. To Big Andy's surprise and delight, he ended up with nine thousand pounds.

Big Andy promptly spent most of his new found wealth on a fertile ten acre farm overlooking Strangford Lough with excellent views of Scrabo Hill beyond. The new farmhouse had a Scrabo-stone fireplace, electric light, and a bathroom with hot and cold running water. Big Andy enjoyed his new found reputation as a land owner of some stature. But he had become so accustomed to building up walls and knocking walls down and building walls up again he couldn't bear to quit the building trade. He decided the best thing to do was continue knocking walls down and building walls up again and let Bertha and the two sons run the farm.

And they did. Bertha, a no-nonsense woman, and the sons, ran the farm so expertly without their father's help, time came when Big Andy had no say in the running of the place, apart from his insistence there should always be a duck egg for his breakfast. With soda bread. Socially, he retained his position as head of the household. But he was only a figurehead. And he knew it.

The rest of the squad at formerly R. J. McKee & Son soon tumbled as to where Big Andy was in the pecking order on the new farm. They taunted Andy that the reason he shouted and bawled so much and threw his weight around on the building site was because he wasn't allowed to open his mouth in his own house. This usually brought an instant reprisal in the form of a clip on the ear if the offender was young and not likely to offer too much in the way of retaliation, or an appeal to the foreman that Andy's family should not be dragged in to the slanging matches if the offender was older.

Now, at the age of fifty-three years, Big Andy thought it was about time a little excitement entered his mundane existence. He'd worked hard all his life. And for what? He took another draw on the pipe then pulled out the blue spotted handkerchief and gave his shiny head another wipe. He squinted over at Jimmy who was still working at the mortice-lock.

"Have ye got it fitted yet?" he called across the room to the apprentice.

Jimmy pushed the panel door closed and smiled as he turned the key and heard the lock click snugly into place. He picked his Stanley screwdriver up from the floor. "Just finished Andy."

Big Andy fished a pocket watch from his overalls. "It's ten to one. Get the oul' cans on. I'm starvin'."

Big Andy made himself even more comfortable on the bag of cement. He puffed on the pipe and watched Jimmy boil the two billy-cans by the flame of a painter's blow-lamp. Time was when they'd have been boiled over a fire of broken sticks and wood shavings at the back of wherever they were working. You couldn't do that when you were four storeys up in the air in a concrete office-block. You had to move with the times. Use a blow-lamp. But at least the tea was still boiled in the wee black can, the way it should be. That was one thing they couldn't do away with. There'd always be the wee black can.

When the cans boiled Jimmy added the tea and sugar. He stirred them and tossed a slosh of milk into each. He handed a can to Andy who was already half way through a farl of soda bread which held a lump of cheese about an inch thick. Jimmy pulled out his own modest sandwiches and sat down beside his mate. All was silence as the pair munched through their delicacies. Big Andy bided his time until Jimmy was ready to start on the first of his two chocolate digestive biscuits.

"D'ye fancy a wee night out?"

Jimmy paused with the McVities half way to his mouth. He looked sideways at his companion.

"A what?"

"A wee night out. You know what I mean. D'ye fancy a wee night out?"

"I don't know what you mean," chuckled Jimmy. "Tell me."

Big Andy nudged Jimmy confidentially. "A wee night out on the town. This Saturday. You and me. And Woodbine. Out for a wee gargle. Then down to Portaferry to the dance. Or up to the

Gala or the Delta in Belfast. I was talkin' to one of J. P. Corry's men the other day when they were deliverin' that load of timber at the yard. He says the weemin at the Gala are just there for the askin'. He says they're man-mad up there."

Jimmy laughed out loud and lowered his can to the floor. He shook his head and set his biscuit on his knee. "A wee night out! At a dance? With you? Are you joking, Andy? You're not serious?"

Big Andy, who had been laying his plans very carefully for many weeks, sensed things were not going the way he wanted. He brought his fist down sharply on Jimmy's outstretched leg, just on the thigh muscle, numbing it instantly. "I am serious! I mean it!," he retorted as Jimmy gasped with pain and rubbed his thigh. "Are ye on? A wee night out?"

Jimmy gathered from the pain in his leg that Big Andy was indeed serious. Very serious. But he still couldn't take it in. "Andy. You can't go to a dance. You know you can't. You're a married man."

The married gentleman sighed patiently and turned to face Jimmy square on. "Exactly. I'm a married man. Isn't that why I want a wee night out. Away from the wife. Away from the trouble and strife." He winked slyly. "I'm a dab hand at the slow foxtrot, y'know."

Jimmy stared at his work-mate. The thought of sixteen stone Big Andy waltzing round the dance floor to the tune of "It's Now or Never" brought a chuckle, which he managed to stifle, to his throat. He still couldn't believe this middle-aged, married, balding man wanted to go to a dance. Without his wife.

"Let me get this right, Andy. You mean you want to go to a dance to pick up a woman?"

Big Andy glared at Jimmy. "Do ye think I couldn't do it?" he demanded. "You young fellas think you know it all. But I could show you a thing or two. I've got experience. And that's what counts. Experience. A woman likes to be treated like a lady. So you have to turn on the oul' charm." Big Andy suddenly launched into conversation with an imaginary dancing partner, adopting a suitably refined mode of speech obviously meant to impress not only Jimmy but the imaginary lady in question as well. "Good evenin', m'dear. Could I have the pleasure of this waltz? I could? Lovely. Do ye come here very often? Only when there's a dance? Oh, that's very interestin'. The band's very good, isn't it? That's a deelightful dress you're nearly wearin'. It's very hot in here. Maybe ye wud care to partake of a drop of fresh air?" Big Andy concluded his dialogue with a flourish of both hands as Jimmy applauded in appreciation.

"Brilliant, Andy! Brilliant stuff!" laughed Jimmy. "I didn't know you had it in you. But tell me. Will it work?"

"Niver been known to fail," snorted Big Andy. "The only woman it niver worked with was Bertha. The wife. I had to chase her. I chased her 'til she caught me. Isn't that why I'm the way I am now. A good man. Just goin' to waste." He stared hard at Jimmy, a pleading look on his well-worn face. "Well? What d'ye say? Are ye game?"

Jimmy scratched his head and frowned. He didn't fancy going to a dance in Portaferry, or Belfast, or anywhere else – and especially not with Big Andy in tow. Not with a married man on the prowl. Somehow, it didn't seem right. It didn't seem right at all. Fortunately he had a ready made excuse. "Count me out, Andy. I'm going to the pictures. With my mate Dinger. Up to the Ritz in Ards. To see Steve McQueen. In *The Great Escape*."

"Look," insisted Andy, "niver mind goin' to see The Great Escape. Come with me and ye'll be takin' part in the great escape. If ye can manage to get me to some oul' dance without Bertha knowin' anything about it. There's plenty of room in the big Austin. Bring Dinger with ye. It'll be great crack!" Big Andy scrambled to his feet and adopted a dancing position with one brawny arm around an imaginary lady's waist - probably the same lady he had earlier invited outside for a breath of fresh air. He held the imaginary lady firmly with his right arm while extending his left diagonally high into the air, his hand supposedly closing gently on the lady's lily-white. Big Andy danced. And sang. "Tea fer two, cha, cha, cha. You fer me, cha, cha, cha. Me fer you, cha, cha, cha................" He stopped in the middle of his Cha-cha and winked broadly at Jimmy. "Well? What do ye say? Will ye go?"

Jimmy nodded. "Andy. If that's the rehearsal, I can't wait to see the real thing," he conceded. "You name the night. I'll be there!"

"Now yer whistlin!" chortled Big Andy. "I'll pick ye up outside Woolies in the Square. Seven o'clock on Saturday night. We'll head down to Portaferry. You and me and Woodbine. And your mate Dinger. But not a word to anybody. If Bertha found out about this I would have to emigrate."

Jimmy put a finger to his lips. Big Andy's secret was safe with him.

Saturday evening was perhaps the warmest and brightest of the whole summer. Jimmy and Dinger stood outside Woolworths. And waited.

"I thought you said these boys would be here at seven o'clock," complained Dinger, a twenty year old with a taste for brightly coloured jackets and trousers and winkle-picker shoes. "It's ten past seven now. There's not even a sign of them!"

Jimmy picked a loose thread from the sleeve of his navy blazer. "Don't worry. They'll be here. They're probably stuck in a pub somewhere. Unless Andy's wife has cottoned on to what he's up to."

Dinger took a comb from his pocket and ran it through his Brylcreemed locks. He checked the result on his reflection in Woolworths window. "What did you say the name of this other character is?"

"Woodbine," replied Jimmy. "Big Andy and Woodbine."

"Big Andy and Woodbine!" snorted Dinger. "What sort of name is Woodbine! How did he get a name like that? Is he some sort of nut?" Jimmy grinned. "Woodbine's okay. It's a nickname. Just like yours. We call him Woodbine because he's always broke and runs about the site asking everybody for the loan of a cigarette until pay-day. But he's good crack." Dinger fine-tuned his Brylcreemed locks. "If they don't hurry up the dance'll be over before we get down there. And why are we goin' to Portaferry? There's a perfectly good dance at the Queens Hall."

"I've already explained," sighed Jimmy. "Big Andy wants to go somewhere he won't be recognized. He'd look well waltzing around the Queens Hall and bumping into his wife's sister, or some of the neighbours. Anyway, it'll be a change of scenery for us."

Dinger pushed his Beatle-type artificial gold rimmed glasses further up on the bridge of his nose. "It's not a change of scenery I'm lookin' for. It's dolly-birds in miniskirts. Hey! Is that them now?"

A powder blue Austin Cambridge with cream wings nicely perforated with red rust holes pulled into the Square a few yards from them, the engine still running noisily. The driver and his front seat companion waved frantically in the general direction of Jimmy and Dinger.

"That's them!" confirmed Jimmy. "That's Big Andy. And Woodbine. Let's go!"

Jimmy and Dinger clambered into the back seat of Andy's patched up Cambridge. Woodbine, a tall skinny youth with yellow shoulder length hair greeted the new arrivals with cigarette laden breath. Big Andy slammed the car into first and roared down the Square and turned left toward the Portaferry Road.

"Ye're lukkin' well, Anderson," quipped Big Andy, studying Jimmy in his rear view mirror as they roared past the Old Cross. "Ye might get off yer mark yerself the night."

Jimmy grinned. "You're not looking too bad yourself, Andy."

Relatively speaking, Big Andy was indeed not looking too bad. The peak cap, which Big Andy was rarely seen without, had been abandoned. What remaining strands of grey hair he still owned had been liberally sprinkled with a sweet-smelling brillantine and carefully laid across his bald pate for maximum effect. The brown suit was well out of fashion and stood a fair chance of being the only one of its type to be on view at the Portaferry dance on this particularly night. But the beige silk tie Big Andy had chosen complemented it perfectly. Andy, who unknown to Bertha enjoyed a little flutter on the gee-gees, had chosen to ornament the tie with a genuine gold-plated tiepin fashioned in the style of two racehorses passing a winning post neck and neck. Jimmy watched Big Andy's hands drumming on the steering wheel. He'd never seen the big man's hands and fingers free from bits of hardened plaster and cement, some of it usually deeply ingrained under his fingernails. The hands were spotless; the nails obviously trimmed, and as far as Jimmy could see, maybe even filed. And the perfectly folded white handkerchief in Big Andy's top pocket proclaimed that here indeed was a man of some social standing.

"Thank ye, Jimmy m'boy," responded the big man in reply to Jimmy's compliment. "I feel, and I think you'll agree, I look like a million dollars. I'm really lukkin' forward to this oul' dance." He half turned in his seat and glanced backwards. "You're goin' to see a bit of action the night, Dinger."

Dinger sniffed. "Hope so," he muttered, without enthusiasm.

Woodbine pulled out a packet of cigarettes and reached it over his shoulder. "D'ye smoke, Dinger?" Dinger accepted the offer and pulled a Woodbine from the ten-pack. Woodbine waved the packet under Big Andy's nose. "What about you, big fella? D'ye want a feg?"

Big Andy shot Woodbine a withering look. "I wuddn't mind a feg. But not one of them rubbish. But you always were a chape Joe." He pulled a packet of Gallaghers Blues from under the dashboard and thrust it at Woodbine. "Light me one of them. And then put the packet back in that glove compartment!"

Woodbine lit the Gallaghers Blue and tossed the match out the window. He blew a circle of smoke into Andy's face and handed him the superior weed.

"What did ye tell Bertha?"

"What about?" grunted Big Andy.

"About where you were goin' the night. What did you tell her?"

"Oh," giggled Big Andy like a small boy who has just successfully raided the biscuit box. "I told her I was goin' to your house. To play a game of draughts. What do you think of that?" He laughed at the simplicity of the deception and how Bertha had fallen for it.

"Draughts!" repeated Woodbine. "You told her you were goin' to play a game of draughts! And you all dressed up like somethin' out of a club book!"

"Don't worry about Bertha," chortled Big Andy. "I know how to handle her." He caught Jimmy's eye in the mirror. "Does yer mate take a drink, Jimmy?"

Dinger answered for himself. "I'm not much for the alcohol, Andy. But I can take a bottle to pass myself. If you know what I mean."

"That's what I like," sniggered Andy. "A man that can pass himself. We'll have a couple of bottles in Portaferry. Before the dance. What d'ye say?"

It was a pleasant run down along the shores of Strangford Lough. The evening sun glittered gold on the calm waters as the big Austin followed the twisting road to the village at the end of the peninsula. When they arrived at Portaferry Big Andy drove along the main street and turned down the steep hill which led to the shore front and a blissful view of Strangford beyond. He turned on to the front then stopped and turned off the ignition. He looked into the rear view mirror and made a slight adjustment to his silk tie. Then he pulled out a comb and scraped it across his head. Satisfied, he slipped the comb back into his pocket. "Right boys. Let's go and get our whistle wet!"

The pub Big Andy had chosen for the wetting of the whistles was small and well filled. Jimmy glanced around, looking for somewhere to sit. Most of the clientele seemed to be farmers or boatmen in for their nightly pint and a bit of a yarn. Each of them of them was every bit as rustic as the pub itself. In the far corner a couple of youths threw darts without any great degree of accuracy or enthusiasm at a papier-mache dart board so riddled with holes it was barely able to support the occasional dart which did happen to strike it. In spite of the warmth of the summer evening a turf fire glowed warmly close to where Jimmy stood. An old man sat in front of the fire playing "I'll Take You Home Again Kathleen" on a red accordion and singing to his own accompaniment. Big Andy and his companions paused in their search for seats to listen to the old man's playing. Jimmy caught the sad far away look in the man's eyes and he wondered what unfulfilled dreams and dashed hopes he had seen in a long lifetime. He could see the man lived for days that were gone, for days that would not come again.

Everyone applauded when the old man finished, and none louder than Big Andy. Then the big man pushed his way farther into the pub to renew the search for seats. At the far end of the bar he bumped against a very large bird cage suspended from the smoke grimed ceiling by a long black chain. In the cage a very large mina bird jumped about on its perch, ruffling its glossy black feathers and taking a sudden and particular interest in Big Andy. It fastened its twinkling eyes on the big man, twisting its head this way and then that.

"Drink up! Drink up! It's closing time! Drink up! It's closing time!" chittered the bird. Since the bird probably offered this advice to the locals every day from sun up to sun down without anybody paying the slightest heed, it stressed upon the stranger even more vehemently the absolute necessity of drinking up without further ado.

Big Andy was taken with the bird immediately. He nudged Jimmy in the ribs. "Listen to that oul' bird. Listen to it cacklin'." Big Andy laughed as the bird repeated its solemn warning once more. Andy put his face close to the cage and eye balled the bird. "Drink up yerself, ye stupid oul' crow! It's nowhere near closin' time! It's only half past eight!" This information, kindly supplied by Big Andy, silenced the bird immediately. It twisted its head and took a couple of studied looks at the big man, eyes twinkling in confusion. Then it hopped away to the farther reaches of its cage, put its head underneath its wing, and spoke not another word for the rest of the night.

The four companions found some seats and a table nobody else seemed to be particularly interested in, possibly because it was in the direct firing line of the afore-mentioned dart-throwers and was frequently subject to straying missiles. Big Andy motioned to his friends to be seated and declared loudly that if any dart struck any one of them, or even the table at which they were sitting, he, Big Andy, would personally pin the thrower of the dart to the board with his very own implement. It may have been coincidence. But the dart throwers suddenly tired of their game and with sullen looks retired to the bar.

Big Andy beamed at Woodbine. "What are ye havin'? I'm buyin'."

"A pint," answered Woodbine, stretching his legs beneath the table.

"And ye'll have a Cream of the Barley to go with it," declared Big Andy." He turned to Jimmy. "Will ye take a pint, Jimmy?"

Jimmy grinned and shook his head. "Andy. You know I never drunk a pint in my life. I tried it once. I just don't like the stuff. I'll take an orange squash."

Big Andy snorted in disgust "I'm buyin' no orange squash! What d'ye think this is? A Sunday School outin? Ye'll take a pint like the rest of us!"

But Jimmy wasn't to be moved. He didn't like alcohol. He didn't like the taste of it and he didn't like the way it scrambled folk's brains. But he met Big Andy half way and agreed to partake of a shandy, on condition he did the mixing of the lemonade and the lager without any direction from Andy. Despite Big Andy's coaxings, and much to the big man's disgust, Dinger also refused the pint and the Cream of the Barley but agreed to take an undiluted Harp Lager. Big Andy sighed in frustration. But when the drinks arrived he paid up cheerfully.

The pub got noisier as the night wore on. Big Andy put away pint after pint, each with a Cream of the Barley, which he said was the best whiskey, to keep them company. The accordion player played and sang and more turf was thrown on the fire and the entire company was as one, with the exception of the mina bird who resolutely rebuffed all attempts to bring it back into the merriment and good cheer of the evening. The man with the accordion struck up "Fine Boy Ye Are" which seemed to put a gleam into his eye and occasioned the entire bar to join in by way of vocal refrain. The till behind the bar rang sweetly, and just as Big Andy seemed perfectly capable of disposing of every drop of alcohol in the pub without being full, so the till appeared capable of taking every penny in the customer's pockets without having to refuse any.

Big Andy downed his fifth Cream Of The Barley, seemingly without any ill effects. He smiled knowingly at his companions. "I can't wait to get into this dance. I've been lukkin' forward to it all week. Keep yer eye on me the night, and ye'll learn a thing or two." He leaned over the table to ensure his friends missed none of his words of wisdom. "Ye see," he continued, tapping his fingers in the beer floating on the table top, "the trouble with you young fellas, regardin' weemin, is, ye have no taste and ye have no...ye have no......"

"Tact?" suggested Jimmy.

"Tact," agreed Big Andy. "Exactly the word I was lukkin' for." He grinned. "Ye always were a good man with the words, Anderson. Anyway, as I was sayin', you young fellas have no....no tact. You'll probably dander into this oul' dance and drag some slip of a wee hussy on to the floor. And ye'll stamp about like a buck eejit doin' this oul' twistin' or jivin' or whatever they call it, and gettin' nowhere." Big Andy stopped at this point in his discourse to let the gravity of his words sink in and to order another round of drinks. "Now. You watch me," he continued when the drinks arrived. "Watch me when I go in. I go for the mature type. That I will not deny. But they need to be good-lukkin as well. I don't just dance with anybody. Anyway, when I see one I fancy, I'll just walk up to her nicely and ask her if she would like to dance. Tact, y'see. Tact. Then, when she says I'd love to, I escort her out to the centre of the floor. I wait for the beat of the music. Then I waltz her round the hall and after two trips, waltz her out the door an' Bob's yer uncle!"

Big Andy laughed heartily at his own description of how things would go once he had gained the dancehall. Jimmy laughed as well though it was plain to see the Cream of the Barley's were now having a decided effect on Big Andy.

It was ten o'clock when the four revellers pushed back their chairs to leave. The mina bird, sensing something was up, caught Big Andy's eye as he made his way out. "Drink up! Drink up! It's closing time!" it cackled, eyes gleaming again.

Big Andy put his face right up against the cage and close to the bird. "It's the first time ye've been right the night, ye stupid oul' crow!" He laughed boisterously and pulled open the pub door. "Come on boys. Let's get into this ballroom and give these weemin a bit of a thrill!"

The ballroom, or to be more precise, dancehall, was just a short walk up the hill from the pub. It was small and unpretentious. The four companions filed through the narrow single door entrance which opened up into a small wood panelled porch. A rather elderly gentleman in a peaked cap, not unlike the type usually favoured by Big Andy, sat just inside the porch at a small table. On the table, built in columns of varying heights, were piles of half crowns, two-shilling pieces, shillings, sixpences, thrupenny bits and a few pennies. The man held a reel of blue cloakroom tickets in his hand. He dourfully issued one to each patron as they filed in for the night's enjoyment.

Big Andy breezed up to the ticket seller and addressed him boldly.

"How much?"

"Nine shillin'," replied the ticket seller tearing off a ticket without bothering to look up.

"Nine bob!" repeated Big Andy incredulously. "Nine shillin's! Are ye mad? I only want to dance in the place. I don't want to buy the hall!" He turned to Jimmy who was directly behind him. "D'ye hear this comedian? He says it's nine bob to get in! D'ye think he's crackers?"

Jimmy shrugged. "It was your idea to come down here. The only thing you can do is pay up. Unless you want to go home again." He pushed past Big Andy and laid down a ten shilling note. He lifted his change and his ticket and nodded to Andy. "Come on. What's nine shillings to a man of your means? You aren't going to disappoint all the ladies in Portaferry for the sake of nine bob? Are you?"

"It's not the nine shillin's," complained Big Andy. "It's the principle. Nine bob to get into a dance! I niver heard the like of it in my life. Niver!" Grudgingly he laid down, one by one, four half-crowns. The gentleman in the peak cap handed him his ticket and a shilling change. Big Andy spat on the shilling and dropped it into his pocket and accompanied his friends into the hall.

The Portaferry dancehall was more spacious than Jimmy had expected from his first impression outside. There were already quite a number of couples dancing and doing their best to avoid another elderly gentleman, also in a peak cap, who was skirting in and out between them throwing French Chalk over the floor and dancers alike without discrimination. Half a dozen coloured light bulbs glowed on each side of the hall. A spotlight from somewhere played on a mirror ball rotating from the ceiling. Big Andy tripped over one of the wooden chairs scattered around the perimeter of the floor for the convenience of those who chose not to dance or were unable to avail themselves of a partner. Dinger nudged Jimmy.

"Is this a dance? Or a wake? Take a look at that band!"

Jimmy had already noticed the band. One accordion player. One fiddler. One drummer. The trio were thumping out "Have I Told You Lately That I Love You" in true country style.

Dinger groaned. "I'm goin' home! Now! I don't believe this! I just do not believe it!"

"How are you going to get home?" laughed Jimmy. "Are you going to walk the whole way back to Ards? Come on. Enjoy yourself. Didn't you used to do these dances in the Young Farmers Club?"

"That was years ago. I can't remember them oul' dances now. I shouldn't have let you talk me into comin' down here. I wish I'd gone to the Ritz to see Steve McQueen."

Woodbine admitted to Dinger that he wasn't awfully impressed with the quality of music on offer, but he was only here for the beer so it didn't really matter. He was going to enjoy himself anyway. Big Andy thought the band was just perfect though he could well understand how anyone brought up on Chubby Checker might well feel ill at ease in the presence of real music. But after all, this was where experience and taste came in.

"I'll say one thing for it," conceded Dinger. "There's plenty of good-lookin' talent here." He winked broadly at Big Andy. "I can't wait to see you in action, big fella!"

He didn't have too long to wait. The big man was already making further adjustments to his tie and sizing up the ladies, those dancing and those standing about in little groups or seated in chairs. Jimmy watched Andy's eyes sweep the room, stopping every now and then at any female who particularly took his fancy.

Jimmy turned to speak to Woodbine. But the gangly Woodbine was already half way round the hall cutting a very fine version of "The Gay Gordons" with a tall thin girl who wore glasses and not much of a skirt. Woodbine's quick and unexpected getaway was an upset for the form book and took the other three completely by surprise.

"It didn't take him long to get going," laughed Jimmy. "I thought you were going to be the star here tonight, Andy."

Big Andy frowned and pointed a finger at Jimmy. "Don't you worry about me. Woodbine won't last the course. He's too impetuous. I like to weigh everything up before I make a move. Just like a game of draughts. Study the board. Make yer move. Win the game!" He laughed. "I might be a slow starter. But I'm a fast finisher!"

"But do you see anything you fancy, big fella," interrupted Dinger, nodding toward the floor.

Big Andy gazed directly across the hall. "You're darn tootin' I do! D'ye see that dame sittin' in the corner? The one with the green dress and red cardigan?"

Jimmy and Dinger followed Big Andy's gaze. They both nodded, unimpressed.

"Well, she hasn't took her eyes off me since I came in."

"That doesn't say a lot," quipped Jimmy. "You're only in the place about three minutes!"

"She fancy's me," insisted Big Andy. "I can tell by the way she's lookin' at me." He grinned. "I'll let her sweat it out for a bit. I'll get her up at the start of the next dance."

Big Andy had just finished speaking when Woodbine swept past, very closely wrapped up in the tall thin girl who wore glasses and not much of a skirt and who seemed to be absolutely delighted with Woodbine's company. Woodbine grinned broadly and gave his friends a confident thumbs up as he disappeared into the crowd. They signalled back and stared at each other in astonishment. Jimmy shook his head. "He turned out to be a dark horse."

"Aye. He's doin' rightly," Big Andy grudgingly acknowledged. "But he'll niver stick the pace. He's just away to a lucky start. That's all."

"He's doin' better than any of us," complained Dinger as the band stamped out the last of "The Gay Gordons" and the dance ended. The couples separated and melted into the crowd of non-dancers at the bottom of the hall. Woodbine elbowed his way back to his three friends.

"Well? What d'ye think of that bird? She goes for me in a big way."

"No class," sniffed Big Andy. "No class at all."

The Master of Ceremonies, a short fat gentleman wearing corduroy trousers and a white polo neck jumper reaching to somewhere about his knees, announced the next dance. It would be a tango – an old fashioned one – and beyond the capabilities of Jimmy and Dinger though Woodbine had already dashed off in search of the tall thin girl who wore glasses and not much of a skirt.

Big Andy cleared his throat and smiled at Jimmy and Dinger. "I suppose this dance'll be a wee bit too much for you to handle. So I'll be sayin' good night to ye now. I'll hardly see you again until it's time to go home. I'll be otherwise engaged. But you know where the car is." He grinned broadly, straightened his tie, and strode casually and with a little swagger in what he imagined was a straight line to where his chosen lady in the green dress and red cardigan sat alone in the corner.

Jimmy and Dinger watched anxiously as Andy staggered across the floor. They didn't think he'd make it. The Cream Of The Barley's were now having their maximum effect on the big man's constitution, sense of direction, and sense of balance. But he completed the journey safely, albeit by a roundabout route, and stood before the lady he had chosen to grace with his company. Jimmy watched Andy lean over the lady, hiding her from view. Some sort of conversation took place. But there didn't seem to be any movement on the part of the lady in the green dress and red cardigan. Big Andy straightened up. He pointed agitatedly to the band and then waved a hand at the dance-floor. He leaned over the lady again. This time the conversation seemed to be somewhat heated. Suddenly there was an arm movement from the lady in the green dress and red cardigan and Jimmy believed Big Andy had successfully completed his mission. But the big man turned abruptly on his heel and strode back across the floor, bouncing dancing couples out of his way as he did so.

"What happened?" gasped Jimmy as Big Andy burst through the dancers and up to him like a runaway express train. "What did you do to her?"

Big Andy's face was purple. "What did I do to her! What did she do to me, ye should be askin'! All I did was ask the oul' hag to dance. She wuddn't get up!" Andy lapsed into a high pitched voice, obviously mimicking the lady concerned. "Oh! You have been drinking," she says. "I do not dance with men that drink."

Big Andy pulled the handkerchief from his top pocket and gave his head a bit of a wipe. He was breathing heavily and quickly. "So I just told her a man would need to have plenty of drink in him before he would ask somebody with a face like hers to dance, because he was hardly likely to do it when he was sober and in full possession of his senses. And then she hit me a skelp in the face. But did ye see her? A face on her like a door-knocker." He mopped his head again and blew his nose. "I've a good notion to report her. Nine bob to get into a dance and the weemin' won't dance. It's ruined my night. Completely ruined it."

"That's the chance you have to take when you ask them up, big fella," chimed in Dinger. "They call it ladies privilege. They don't have to get up if they don't want to."

"That's right, Andy," agreed Jimmy. "It's just the chance you take. They don't have to get up. You know that." But there was no consoling Big Andy. His confidence was shattered. He was a helpless dispirited hulk as Jimmy and Dinger dragged him to a chair at the back of the hall and sat him down. Andy collapsed into the chair and sat motionless, his head in his hands. Jimmy and Dinger tried everything they knew. But there was no comforting Big Andy. Finally he lifted his head long enough to advise Jimmy and Dinger to get on to the dance floor and see what they could do for themselves. As for him, he would sit where he was until it was time to go home.

Dinger didn't need further coaxing. Although he had no idea how to tango the sight of a crowded floor and a good-looking blonde close by were sufficient encouragement for him to make an attempt at it. He disappeared like a greyhound out of a trap at Dunmore Stadium.

Jimmy stood by Big Andy. He wasn't a dancer. He'd only come on this escapade to please the big man who now slumped miserably in his chair. He barely looked up as the dark horse Woodbine tangoed past with the tall thin girl who wore glasses and hardly any skirt, and cutting such a dashing figure Jimmy could hardly believe it was the same scrawny youth he toiled with every day on the building site. Dinger stumbled past, trying vainly to adapt the music of the old fashioned tango to fit that of a slow waltz, with the good-looking blonde. The fact that his feet and the music were at distinct odds with each other didn't seem to be spoiling in any way his enjoyment of the dance.

Suddenly Big Andy stirred himself. He lifted his head and threw his shoulders back in something of his former style. "Going to dance?" asked Jimmy as the big man got to his feet and ran his handkerchief over his head. "I'm goin' to do no such thing" retorted Big Andy. "And I do not know what possessed me to come down to this place! I don't know why I did it. I have a nice wee home, and a nice wee wife in it, waitin' for me. I have no need to be rakin' about the countryside chasin' after weemin'. And especially not that one in the green dress and red cardigan. She's not in the same league as my Bertha. As fine a woman as ever milked a cow, Bertha is. And the best cook in the townland. In the whole County Down, if goes to that." He raised his hand as Jimmy sought to interrupt. "Now, don't get me wrong Jimmy. The crack was great. But don't you iver coax me out on one of these wild goose chases again. I know you young fellas have to gad about 'til ye find the wumman of yer choice. But I found mine. Long ago. I'm happy enough in my own home. With wee Bertha." He took his hankie and gave his shiny pate, which gleamed as it caught the reflection of the revolving mirror-ball, another wipe. He stuck the handkerchief back in his top pocket and wagged a finger at Jimmy. "It's a true sayin'. Home is where the heart is. And that's where my heart is. At home." Having finished this discourse Big Andy rested his case, and sat down.

That's when Jimmy saw her – the merest glimpse – between the dancing couples as they swept past. He lost her, then found her again. Suddenly, there was no one in the dancehall but her.

Maybe she nineteen. Maybe twenty. But the prettiest girl Jimmy had ever laid eyes on, and from that moment, the prettiest he ever wished to see. He took a step forward. The girl was laughing. Her high cheek bones and dark eyes reminded him of Ava Gardner whom he'd seen only last week in *Showboat* at the Ritz. But Ava Gardner's hair was black. The girl's hair was dark copper and shone richly each time the light from the mirror- ball caught it. But it was the underlying gentleness and kindness Jimmy read in the laughing face that drew him immediately to her.

She dressed well too. Simply. But well. A white gypsy blouse and a wide flared skirt with a large print of red roses. A narrow red sash circled her waist She wore no jewellery save a tiny gold crucifix hanging at her throat.

Jimmy glanced down at Big Andy. The big man appeared to have taken refuge from the woes of life in that soother of all pains, sleep. He looked over again to where the girl sat with her companion. Jimmy's eyes followed the two youths making their way toward the girls. He frowned. Should he move quickly and ask the girl to dance, even though he had no idea how to tango? If he didn't, it wouldn't be long until someone else did. Or should he take the chance she would be free for the next dance? Not much hope of that, he thought. Desperately he looked around for Woodbine. Or Dinger. Anybody, to look after Big Andy. But the two ladies-men were lost in the crowded dance-floor.

One of the two youths stopped right in front of the girl. Too long, Jimmy reprimanded himself. He'd waited too long. Just as he always did. He looked on as the youth and the girl engaged in conversation which seemed to go on and on and on. Then the girl smiled and shook her head. The youth shrugged and turned away.

Jimmy wasted no further time pondering his abilities, or lack of them, at the old-fashioned tango, or whether Big Andy would continue to sleep or fall in a drunken stupor to the floor. In five purposeful strides he stood before the girl.

"Pardon me. Would you like to dance?"

The words tumbled from Jimmy's mouth before he realized he had spoken them and suddenly he wished he could take them back. This girl could have her choice of anyone in the hall. Anyone. Why would she want to dance with him? The girl looked at him with gentle brown eyes. She hesitated. Her complexion was soft and clear and showed little sign of needing help from make-up of any sort for the flush on her cheeks came from within. There was only a trace of pale lipstick on her mouth. She smiled, a warm smile. Her eyes twinkled.

"I'm afraid I don't tango very well."

"Me neither," admitted Jimmy. "Maybe we could help each other? This is the last set."

The girl looked at her companion. She smiled again at Jimmy and got to her feet. "Well, if you're sure you want to take the chance!"

Jimmy guided the girl to the centre of the floor, hardly able to believe his good fortune. But he knew he would need more than fortune to get through the tango without making a complete idiot of himself.

However little the girl knew about the old-fashioned tango it was at least twice as much as Jimmy knew. Embarrassed, he apologized over and over again. But the girl accepted all his toe-tramping mistakes with good grace. Together they laughed their way through the set. When it ended Jimmy shook his head ruefully.

"That wasn't much fun for you," he apologized again. "Maybe you'll give me a chance to redeem myself in the next dance?"

The girl laughed and tossed her head back. "You weren't all that bad. And I made as many mistakes as you did."

That was generous. Jimmy knew he'd been a total disaster and he told the girl so. "But let's hope the next dance is more suited to both our styles. And especially mine. By the way, my name's Jimmy. What's yours?"

"Noreen. Noreen Emmett."

"Noreen," repeated Jimmy. He liked the name. "Noreen. It's an unusual name."

Noreen smiled, the brown eyes lighting up. "Not really. It was my grandmother's name. She came from County Kerry. It's a common enough name down there. That was years ago, of course. She died before I was born. But my father insisted I be called for her. So there you are. A personal potted history of my name. At no extra expense." They laughed together.

"What about Emmett?" asked Jimmy. "I don't suppose you're related to Robert Emmett?"

Noreen looked at him, eyebrows knitting together in curiosity. "I see you're well versed in Irish history. I take it you mean THE Robert Emmett?"

"That's the one," laughed Jimmy. "THE Robert Emmett."

Noreen shook her head. "No. I can't say I can lay claim to being descended from that Robert Emmett. What about you? Any famous ancestors?"

"No," said Jimmy. "No famous ancestors. But we've gone all serious. I didn't mean to bore you."

"You're not the least boring," replied Noreen. "Not in the least"

Jimmy smiled as the Master of Ceremonies announced the next dance. A waltz. "I think your feet will be comparatively safe this time," he murmured as they glided away to the strains of "The Tennessee Waltz."

Noreen smiled too, and laid her head gently against Jimmy's cheek. He held her just a little more tightly and breathed in the faint whisper of her fragrance. Suddenly he was glad, very glad, Big Andy had coaxed him to come down to Portaferry. For a wee night out.

Big Andy's failed wee night out remained, at Andy's request, a closely guarded secret. It had been a rush of blood to the head, he explained to his three comrades before they set off on the journey home, and he should never have let himself be talked into such a foolish venture. He would deem it a great favour if the night was never mentioned to another living soul.

And Big Andy never again ventured on a wee night out. But he had plenty of wee nights in, around the fireside with his wee spouse Bertha, for what more could a married man want than the company and support of a good loyal wife – aye, and two sons who ran the farm every bit as well as he could have run it himself. His days at R. J. McKee & Sons were over. But he never forgot his old workmates. And especially Jimmy. Often times he invited Jimmy and Noreen up to the farmhouse for a wee bit of crack. And especially in the winter time when the nights were cold and wet and a lashing rain drove up the Lough.

"Bring Noreen up to the house, any night you want," encouraged Big Andy. "Sure it's tough enough doin' your coortin' an' the snow fallin' round yer feet and there's no shelter in the hedges at all! Bring her up. Bring her up for a wee night in."

And Jimmy did. Often. Brought Noreen up for a wee night in at Big Andy and Bertha's warm and comfortable fireside where Andy impressed upon Jimmy the well known fact that there is no pleasure upon earth worthy to be compared to the joys and comforts of a happily married life. Jimmy always nodded in understanding. But once in a while, when he was sure no one else could see, he smiled broadly and winked at Big Andy. Big Andy grinned and winked back. They didn't speak a word about it. But the pair of them knew they'd never forget the night they journeyed down to Portaferry. For a wee night out.

The Stranger on Christmas Eve

The old man lifted the big iron poker. He prodded the dying embers of greying turf in the fireplace and shivered. Not with cold. With fear.

He'd known the storm was coming. There was no mistaking the signs. Since early morning he'd watched the clouds build in the western sky, huge, black, and menacing. They'd piled up, one on top of the other, a mass of heavy darkness coming ever nearer. By late afternoon an uneasy stillness hung over the isolated cottage sitting high on the cliff-top – a stillness compounded by an eerie silence as the birds of the garden suddenly ceased from their chattering and deserted the trees and bushes in a unison of fluttering wings.

It was almost dark when the first flakes of snow came scurrying in, and with the snow the wind, the harsh biting wind which now howled and shrieked and moaned through the laurel bushes and the naked sycamore trees like a thousand demented banshees. It whistled under the door and skitted around the old man's sparsely furnished room, threatening to snuff out the feeble light of the two candles on the mantlepiece and leave the cottage in darkness.

The old man, thin and weary and tired of life's journey, looked on as the candles flickered erratically With anxious eyes he watched the tiny white flames as they were harassed by the whistling wind. The flames danced away from each candle as if they had a life of their own, then settled back to catch a precarious hold on the wick once more. The old man sighed with relief. He didn't want to be in darkness tonight. Not tonight. Not tonight, of all nights, when the very forces of hell itself seemed to be ranged against him and his little cottage.

But it wasn't the force of the storm raging outside which struck the cold dagger of fear into his heart. If only it was. But it wasn't. It was the memory of what had happened on this night all those years ago, and the awful fear that the matter was not yet settled, and what had happened then was in some way responsible for the terror that was gripping him now. He tossed the poker into the hearth and glanced at the big clock standing in the chimney corner. In another hour it would be Christmas Day. He would be glad when the black spidery hands of the clock passed midnight. Then it would be another day, a new day, not this day which was the anniversary of that awful day. And on the new day perhaps he would find refuge from the fear and anguish and sorrow tormenting his heart.

But there it was again. The knocking on the door. The knocking which paralysed him with fear and drained the blood from his thin face. He gripped the arms of his chair tightly, so tightly his knuckles became knobs of bony whiteness against the darkness of the wood. Beads of sweat broke out on his forehead.

Why didn't it stop! Why didn't it go, leave him in peace. He'd suffered enough. More than enough. Why didn't it go away! He covered his ears with his hands, trying to delude himself there was nothing there. Maybe it wasn't really a knock at the door. It could be anything - the branches of the old elm scraping the door, the rattle of the latch in the wind – anything, except the knock he knew it to be.

And if it was a knock? What then? Wasn't that what he had yearned for? All these years? Lived for, hoped for, prayed for, and yet dreaded. Didn't he believe, with all the faith in his being that all was not lost, and one night the knock would come to the door and then he would have ease and contentment in his heart and he could die at last in peace? And yet it was the knock on the door which he feared, feared above all things.

There it was again. Not really a knock. Taps. Three of them. Tap. Tap. Tap. Gentle. Not loud, yet somehow plainly audible above the roaring of the wind and the crashing of the wild sea on the jagged rocks at the foot of the cliff. The old man picked up the poker again. He banged it noisily against the side of the hearth, afraid to admit he was afraid, trying to drive away his fear with the noise of metal on stone. But he shuddered as the knocks continued. Tap. Tap. Tap. He moaned, a long low moan, like a trapped and frightened animal, then hurled the poker to the floor and jumped to his feet. Better to face whoever and whatever it was, for what had he to fear but death itself, and life or death had long ago ceased to be of any importance to him. He jumped up from his chair and strode across the hard earthen floor to the dark doorway. His hand trembled as he laid it on the big iron key of the lock on the strong wooden door. He took a deep breath and gripped the key tightly. Then he hesitated as doubt and fear engulfed him even more forcefully than before. He wanted to open the door. He had to open the door. And he couldn't do it. He couldn't bring himself to turn the key, settle the matter for once and for ever. He couldn't turn the key.

Tap. Tap. Tap. Now the sound drove him beyond his senses and beyond reason and beyond fear and beyond anything fear could do to him. He gripped the key even more strongly than before, turned it, and flung the door open wide.

The force of the tempest raging outside ripped past him and knocked him breathless as it slammed him against the wall. The wind roared around the inside of the cottage like a demented demon seeking a home. It snuffed out the two candles instantly and hurled them to the floor, plunging the cottage into blackness. The old man struggled for breath as the icy snow swirled in through the open door and lashed his face and stung his eyes and now there was darkness without and darkness within and whatever vague form stood before him in the doorway it was not the form he expected to see.

"Who's there!" he shouted hoarsely, almost pleadingly, into the darkness. "Who's there I say! Speak up, can't you? Speak up!"

The voice which answered was soft and low. Yet, like the tapping on the door it was plainly audible above the screech and roar of the blizzard.

"Good evening. Could I seek a little shelter from the storm?"

There was no anxiety in the voice. No haste. No pleading. No desperation. Certainly no threat. Just the quiet simple request for shelter, and so meekly made the old man was certain if he refused the owner of the voice would take his leave and be gone without asking a second time. But confused and frightened as he was, the old man would turn no one from his door. And especially not tonight. Not tonight, of all nights.

"Come in! Come in quickly!" he shouted to the figure in the dark doorway. "Go on into the fire while I secure the door!" He stood aside as the tall figure murmured his thanks and eased his way into the cottage. With a great effort the old man laid his weight against the door and forced it shut against the raging storm. He leaned against it and breathed heavily. When he had somewhat recovered he turned the heavy key and securely locked the door. The fear had left him now and he rebuked himself for his foolishness. But as he turned into the room he was surprised to see the two candles burning brightly without a flicker on the mantlepiece, exactly where they had been before he'd opened the door.

The stranger caught his startled look. "I hope you do not mind? Light is always better than darkness."

The old man relaxed and returned the stranger's smile. "True. But it is not easy to keep candles lit on such a night. The storm....it's....it's frightening. The worst I have known." He hurried toward the stranger. "But take off your coat. Hang it there by the chimney-breast. I'll build up the fire. You'll soon be warmed. You'll take some broth?"

The stranger smiled easily. He removed his garment and hung it in the chimney breast "Please. I am grateful. Thank you."

The old man piled the logs on the fire until they crackled and blazed and spat sparks up the chimney and out into the hearth. He laid a small iron pot in the centre of the furnace and studied his unexpected guest as he stirred the contents slowly. He could not make a guess at the man's age. The face and eyes were gentle and understanding, attributes not usually found in the young. But the man's visage held none of the tell-tale signs of ageing. That he was a gentleman, there was no doubt. His whole bearing and manner declared it. But who was he? Why was he abroad on such a night as this, with the snow as high as a man's thigh? The old man's natural curiosity sought answers to these and many other questions. But his own good manners restrained him from enquiring directly from his guest.

The soup was near to boiling and the leaping flames of the fire threw dancing shadows across the room as the old man ladled a goodly measure into a wooden soup bowl. He passed it to the stranger with a small piece of rough bread.

"I am sorry the meal is so frugal," he apologized as the stranger took the bowl. "But my needs are few, and my tastes simple. But please, consider my dwelling, humble though it is, your own. I am very glad of your company on such a night."

The stranger nodded his thanks. He took the soup and bread from the old man and closed his eyes. He smiled as he opened them again.

"Humble is best An abundance of possessions do not necessarily bring happiness. I have known many who struggled for wealth and the vanities of this life only to find at last these things were as ashes in the mouth. But to live a simple life ... ah, there is happiness indeed ..."

The old man filled his bowl and nodded as he scrutinized the stranger again by the light of the fire.

"These are words of wisdom, sir. And in my own case I had to be brought very low before I learned the truth of them. But the passing of years and trials of life bring many a hard lesson which might have been more easily learned. And some of us are more stubborn to be taught than others." He laid his spoon in his bowl and looked earnestly at the stranger, unable to restrain his curiosity any longer. "But tell me sir. How do you come to be here tonight? My cottage is far from the common way. The path is narrow and not much used, and dangerous on such a night. How do you come to be here? What is your transport?"

The stranger set his bowl in the hearth. He leaned back in his chair. "There is no great mystery. I have certain business which needs to be settled tonight. As for my transport, it is simple. I travel on foot. I have occasion to meet many people so it suits my purpose well, and I miss none with whom I would speak, if they are willing to hear me. The pace is slow. But haste abounds on every hand. Who is the better for it? To move quietly and slowly through the world brings its own rewards."

The old man stared again at the stranger, trying once more to take a bearing on his age. But he could not do it. "Well said, sir," he replied as he picked up his spoon again. "But tonight? Why do you wander about the countryside on a night like this? A person could perish in the elements which are abroad tonight. Did you take a wrong turning? In the darkness?"

The stranger shook his head. "I make no error. I am not lost. And my journey tonight is necessary."

The old man shivered as the wind whistled around the cottage. He lifted the poker and stirred up the fire. He rubbed his hands in the blaze as the sparks and flames and heat roared up the chimney. "Thank God I have no need to be out on such a night. And God help those who are."

The stranger sat upright in his chair. He fixed his gaze on the old man.

"You believe in God?"

The old man looked up. The directness of the question caught him off guard and disturbed him and a ready answer was not upon his lips. There had been a time – a long time ago – when he could have responded immediately and given good reason for his response. But he was older now. Wiser. And yet, perhaps not wiser. But he would not give a glib answer to the question which had so abruptly faced him with all his beliefs, and with all his doubts. The stranger's question troubled him and he tried to fend off the challenge.

"Why do you ask such a question sir? Is not this Christmas Eve? It wants but a few moments to midnight when all the world will celebrate the birth of the Son of God. Why do you ask such a question?"

The stranger's gaze did not falter. It remained fixed on the old man's eyes, holding him.

"You mentioned the name of God. Not once. Twice. The name falls from the lips of many who know nothing and care less about the One of whom they speak. Do you thank God in sincerity? Or are your words merely words?"

The old man lowered his eyes, unable to bear the searching gaze of the stranger. It was a little while before he spoke and when he did his voice was barely audible above the storm outside.

"Yes. Yes… I think I believe in God," he murmured, eyes on the floor.

"Yet your answer lacks assurance," pressed the stranger. "Why is this?"

The old man sighed, a long deep sigh. The stranger's probing questions unsettled him, made him uncomfortable, almost angry. They were questions he had asked himself many times through the years since that night, questions which troubled him, questions which thus far remained unanswered. He lifted his head slowly and gazed for a long time at a faded picture hanging in the centre of the chimney breast. The picture was of a young girl with long flowing hair the colour of corn – a girl of pleasant features and form and not long left childhood.

"Sir," replied the old man, his eyes still upon the picture, "believing in that which we cannot see demands faith, and some would say this is foolishness. But there was a time when I had this faith and I believed nothing could ever shake it. But I am an old man now, and have seen many things. I see a wicked world go on it's way rejoicing while those who would temper this life with their goodness and kindness, and whom the world can ill afford to be without, are taken from it." Here the old man ceased from speaking, hoping to draw a response, agreement even, from the stranger. But no response came. The stranger remained silent, head tilted slightly, and the old man felt obliged to continue. "As I said, there was a time when my faith was strong. Life was good and I loved it. All of it. The trees on the hills and the gentle wave of the yellow cornfield beneath the summer sun. The ascending of the lark and the melody of the song-thrush – all these were a delight to me. And to add to my joy I was blessed with a good wife who saw the world as I did and was always by my side. But when our daughter came my wife was taken, and sadness entered my life. Great sadness. Times became hard. But I raised my daughter, my only child, and sought to implant within her gentle heart all that was good and beautiful and true. Together we roamed these hills and valleys and walked by the seashore. My daughter loved the sea, even in its wildest moods. And in spite of all my grief I could still say I believed in God."

The stranger nodded. "And then?"

The old man sighed. "And then came the time of my greatest grief, greater grief than I had ever known. Then came the time when that which I loved more than life itself was taken from me and my once happy heart was smashed and broken, and my spirit with it. A man can only take so much suffering…"

Once more the old man fixed his eyes on the picture of the young girl. His voice faltered as he struggled to continue. "It was… twenty years ago. Twenty years ago, on this very night. My daughter was swept from this headland to her death in the sea and rocks below." The old man turned his head to the stranger. "If only you could have known her, sir. She was beautiful. And not only to gaze upon. She was as honest and true as the new-born day, full of life, and the joy of living. But her life was taken, and mine may as well have been, for I see neither purpose nor plan in it. Often, on a winter night, I sit here by the fire. Alone. Sometimes I think I can hear her voice calling to me on the wind and the sighing of the sea." He paused. "And sometimes… sometimes I think I hear her knock upon the door, coming back to me after all these years, believing she would come back, yet not understanding how. And when I heard your knock tonight…"

The stranger nodded. "Death is common to all men, and none can boast of tomorrow. Great sorrow is the price we must pay for great love, and only the heart that bears it can know the pain. I speak from experience. I too have shed tears and grieved at the loss of one who was very dear to me. But did not God comfort you in all these things and give you promises to cheer your heart?"

The old man nodded. "Indeed. Many comforts. And many promises. I could not have borne the grief and pain had it not been so."

"And was not one of these the assurance that the last enemy to be destroyed was death itself?"

"That, and many others," agreed the old man, a gleam of light coming into his dull grey eyes. "I see you are well acquainted with the scriptures, sir. And there was a time when I found all my comfort and joy within those pages. But the years have dealt harshly with me. Sorrow has been piled upon sorrow and my heart has become cold and bitter. I have become a man of little faith. God is far from me. I wait daily for the silver cord to be loosed that I might depart this world perchance to find a better. I have nothing to offer heaven, or earth either."

The stranger leaned forward in his chair. "Why do you say these things? How can you say you are lonely and cast out when the God of all comfort has promised to be by your side for ever and ever? And as for having nothing to offer on earth, have you not this night taken a stranger, one unknown to you, under your roof, and given him food and shelter?"

The old man lowered his eyes. "Sir. Your words greatly shame me, and I know the truth of them very well. But I no longer live in the power and strength of them. If I could only know indeed that I am not forsaken it would mean more to me than all earthly treasures." He lifted his arms and spread them open. "As for what I have done for you… it is nothing. Anyone would do the same on a night such as this."

"Not so," countered the stranger. "I knock on many doors. Few are opened to me, and I must pass on. But sometimes, sometimes the door is opened and I am invited in to sup, even as you have invited me in this evening."

As the stranger finished speaking the clock in the corner chimed the first stroke of midnight. The old man looked up.

"It is Christmas Day," he murmured. "Christmas Day, when all the world rejoices. Forgive me sir for my long outburst of speech, and for the coldness of my heart. It may be I have been too long without agreeable company and have forgotten my manners. But it is Christmas Day, and I hope it will be a happy day for you, as happy as any you have known."

The old man and the stranger talked for a long, long time, until the old man's eyes became heavy and the gentle shades of sleep drew ever nearer. He rose from his chair and pulled back the ragged cloth covering the window panes.

"The storm still rages. You will stay the night? It will not be necessary for you to journey farther in the darkness tonight?"

The stranger smiled. "The darkness holds no terrors for me.

But I thank you for your kind invitation. I will indeed abide under your roof this night. I thank you."

The old man held up a hand. "Please. Do not thank me. You have been a great encouragement to my heart this night. The world is a cold and lonely place and every man seeks his own happiness. Few have time or inclination to utter a word of comfort or cheer to the broken-hearted. It is I who should thank you. And I do. Thank you, sir."

The old man lifted the poker and scattered the dying embers of the fire. He picked up one of the candles, which had burnt low, from the mantlepiece, and pointed to a tiny room leading off the wall opposite the fireplace.

"Please sir, if you will step this way. The room is humble enough, but the bed is comfortable. I trust it will serve your needs for the night and leave you refreshed for your journey on the morrow."

The stranger followed the old man into the tiny chamber which held nothing more than a simple bed, a small table, and a wooden chair. "But this is your bedroom. And I see no other. I hesitate to take advantage of your kindness."

The old man waved a dismissive hand. "It is nothing. Many times I fall asleep in my chair before the fire and do not waken until the shades of morning stream through the window panes. I will be comfortable there." He set the candle on the chair beside the bed. "If you have need of anything further, please, knock upon the door. I will attend to it. I trust you will sleep well. Good night, sir."

The old man drew the door behind him, extinguished the remaining candle on the mantlepiece, and settled down for the night in front of the fire.

The dazzle of morning sunlight streaming through the frosted window panes glinted on the glass of the clock face and threw the glare back in the old man's eyes. He stirred in his chair as the last vestiges of sleep departed from him and he became aware of the light playing on his eyes and the coldness of the room. His eyes blinked open as he suddenly remembered. He stared at the burnished brass circle of the clock face which gleamed so brightly he was unable to make out the position of the black hands. Not that time was important. But he could tell by the angle of the sun striking through the tiny window it was already late in the morning and he did not usually slumber so long. Then he remembered it was Christmas day and he sat bolt upright as he recalled again the stranger in his bedroom a few feet away.

The old man turned quickly in his chair and looked toward the other room. The door was still closed. It did not surprise him. The stranger would not avail himself of the facilities of the household until his host had first risen and bade him to do so. He pushed his chair away from the dead fire and shuffled to the door, reproaching himself for his lack of courtesy. He knocked lightly on the door. There was no reply. He waited, then knocked again.

"Sir? It is morning. The storm has abated and I am about to prepare breakfast. I would be honoured if you would join me at your convenience?"

Again, there was no response. The old man leaned his head against the door, listening for the sound of movement within the room. There was none. He knocked again, louder than before, his head still leaning on the door.

"Sir?"

Still there was only silence from within, a silence which confused the old man. But he was reluctant to turn the handle and enter the chamber without invitation. He stood back from the door and knocked upon it loudly, so loudly there could not be any possibility of not being heard. He waited. In vain.

Slowly, and with not a little concern, the old man reached forward and laid his hand upon the cold handle of the door. He turned it gently, waited, then gave the door a little push. It swung open, easily, but not enough to let him see fully into the room. He could see the chair and part of the small table but nothing of the bed. Gently, he pushed the door again. Farther and farther and farther it squeaked upon its hinges until it was wide open. Almost the entire room was open to his view. Wondering, he stepped inside.

The room was empty. Apart from the bed and the few sticks of furniture, there was nothing there. The bed was carefully made up just as it had been the previous night. The old man glanced down at the candle on the chair. It was a shapeless lump of grey wax, long since extinguished. But of the stranger there was no sign. He had gone, evidently taking advantage of the fine morning, anxious to be about his business, yet taking his leave carefully and quietly without disturbing his host.

The old man withdrew from the room and closed the door behind him. He sighed. Few visitors came to his cottage, and fewer still with the wisdom and understanding of the stranger. There were many things he had wanted to say to the stranger, many questions he wanted to ask, more words of truth and encouragement he had wanted to glean from this gentle person whose name he did not even know. Where had the stranger come from? Where was he going? What was the important business which caused him to be abroad on such a night as last night? Would he pass this way again? These and many other questions flooded his thoughts as he made his way to the front door and pulled at it. Maybe he could catch a glimpse of the man along the frost-rimed road, call him back, invite him to stay a little longer.

The door would not open. The old man pulled at it again, impatiently. It remained firmly closed. He pulled even more forcefully at the latch. But the door refused to yield. It was only when he looked down at the key in the lock he understood why. The key was still turned, just as he had turned it last night to secure the lock and the door after the stranger had entered. The old man immediately turned to the smaller door at the rear of the house. It too was secured, the heavy black bolts shot into their keepers. The old man shook his head in dismay and confusion. He pulled back the two bolts from the small door and stepped out to survey the damage the storm had wrought during the night.

The sun was a fiery red orb in the clear winter sky. But for all its great show it lacked strength and did nothing to take the cold from the morning air. The grass was stiff with a white frost. But despite the snow blizzard of last night no snow lay upon the ground. Only the hard frost which rimed the sycamore trees and iced the rain-barrel.

The old man stared up at the naked branches of the trees. The frosted fingers sparkled against the blue sky, every branch intact. Not a twig had fallen to the ground. The laurel bushes had not shed a single leaf and the winter chrysanthemums, white and bronze, stood upright and in full bloom, not a stem bruised or broken. He smiled ruefully. There had been no storm. No snow. And no stranger. Nothing but the dreams of an old man who now, more and more often and for longer and longer periods of time, dwelt in a comforting twilight world of visions and memories of days that used to be.

But the dreams were always good dreams, and the memories they evoked precious. And where else could he find refuge and solace to face the rigours of each new day in his lonely life? And this dream, last night, had been a good dream, and he had learned much from it and his heart was lighter now than it had been for many a long day.

The old man turned back into the cottage to light the fire and warm up his little home. As he moved toward the fireplace his eye immediately fell upon a soup bowl at the side of the hearth. He reached down and lifted it up. He smiled. At least the soup had been real enough, and as good a broth as ever he had prepared. He was about to turn away when something else caught his eye. Another soup bowl – at the other side of the hearth – with a spoon, and the remains of some broth.

The old man's hand shook as his eye travelled from the soup bowl in the hearth to the side of the chimney breast. A long coat hung there – a sort of cloak affair. He gasped involuntarily as the bowl slipped from his fingers and smashed against the hard floor. He moved slowly toward the corner, reaching out for the cloak, yet afraid to lay his hand upon it. With a great effort he forced himself to touch the garment. Slowly he ran his fingers the full length of it. Then he clutched it tightly, with both fists, pulling it close to his face, smelling and feeling the dampness still within its folds.

The old man's hands fell away from the cloak. He stood motionless, staring at it for a long time, trying to understand. He turned his head to the other corner, the corner where the big clock stood tall on the floor surrounded by his jumble of books. The books were piled high, old books, not in any order, but balancing one on top of the other in a careless heap. He moved quickly across the fireplace and grabbed the first book which came to his hand. He looked at it with barely a glance and tossed it aside. He picked up another, and another, plundering through the pile until his hand finally fell on the volume he sought.

The old man opened the book. There had been a time when this had been his favourite of all books, a book whose pages and words he knew almost by heart. But the volume had lain neglected in the corner for a long time, its cover battered and dusty. The old man wiped away the dust with the cuff of his tattered sleeve and feverishly turned the pages. His fingers flicked through them, now forwards, now backwards, stopping, starting, and going on again before stopping for a final time. He stabbed his finger down heavily on a line of print. Nodding in understanding, he read the words aloud.

Be not afraid to entertain strangers, for thereby some have entertained angels unawares.

The old man sank down on his knees, great tears of joy streaming from his eyes. Sobbing loudly he clutched the book to his breast. Last night had been no dream. The storm was real. The stranger had been real. The stranger had talked with him and supped with him and taught him and encouraged him. And he knew now he was not cast aside nor forgotten, and he knew for a certainty there were more things in heaven and earth than he had ever realized and whatever forces had been brought to bear against him and his little cottage last night, the stranger had overcome them all. He had completed his business and restored to him the joy of this present life and given him hope for that which was yet to come. Never again would he seek nor fear the knock upon the door.

And now it was indeed Christmas Day, the day when all the world rejoiced. And he too would rejoice and be glad in it, even as he would rejoice and be glad for all the days remaining to him as he journeyed through this world toward his heavenly home.

A Belfast Christmas Eve

The snow began to fall, gently, silently, as it should but so seldom does, on Christmas Eve. I turned up my collar and pulled my warm gloves a little more comfortingly on my fingers. The day had been bitterly cold in Belfast. I looked forward to returning to the warm happiness of my home and my little family who waited for me. As the snow fell, virgin and clean, it transformed the city centre drabness into a wonderland of sparkling whiteness beneath the yellow glow of the street lamps. Suddenly this was the Christmas Eve of story books and Christmas card scenes, and if the old city had already immersed itself in the spirit of the season, now it perfectly glowed with goodwill and good cheer and peace to all men. The trams, red and black and gold, and packed with last minute shoppers, moaned tediously along the snow covered tracks in Royal Avenue. Red trolley buses swathed along, almost silently, the sparks from their overhead power lines flashing blue against the darkening sky and adding yet another touch of magic to the snowy scene.

The drifting snow filled the Salvation Army carol singers at the junction of High Street and the Avenue with a new enthusiasm as they sang out the old carols over and over and over again. They sang them all – *Away in a Manger*, *Good King Wenceslas* and *Hark the Herald Angels Sing*. And *Silent Night*. The smiling happy faces of the carollers shone with brightness which came not from the yellow glow of the candle-lit lanterns they held aloft, but from that glow which comes from within, from hearts overflowing with joy. The snow deepened and the sudden quietness which hung over the city seemed to be accentuated with every falling flake. So many people – even this late on Christmas Eve – street traders, everywhere, still trying to sell Christmas wrapping paper at tuppence a sheet. And here at the corner of Castle Street, the hot chestnut man sending sparks of gold shooting into the snowy air as he poked among the red-hot cinders of his coke fire. The snow was good snow, not wet mushy snow, and it crunched softly but firmly beneath my feet as I trudged along the Avenue.

One by one the stores began to close and their doors were locked and barred as the shop assistants pulled their coats around them and dashed away to prepare for Christmas in their own home. Home was the place to be on Christmas Eve. But each window of the locked up shops still threw back a kaleidoscope of colour and tinsel and garland and fairy lights as it sought to outdo its neighbour in its presentation of the Christmas season. John Collier, the window to watch, had everything the modern gentleman needed for this cold and icy season – long woollen overcoats, warm scarves, and the very best of leather gloves, all covered with sparkling tinsel and modelled by motionless mannequins with the film star looks of Tyrone Power and Errol Flynn and Rock Hudson all standing in thick cotton wool snow. The more exclusive ladies shops projected the feeling of outer iciness and inner warmth by wrapping their Ava Gardner models in long mink coats and fur hats and boots. And the Belfast shops didn't disappoint the children on that Christmas Eve. I observed the joy and eagerness and expectation etched on the face of every child who stared wide eyed at the host of wonderful things – everything a child could wish for – just out of reach beyond the frosted windows. How their little cheeks glowed with cold and excitement as they pulled at their parent's hands and pointed with glee. Train sets – electric train sets – travelled round and round a snow-flecked track while the Dinky Toys – Morris Minors and Austin Sevens and Ford Anglias waited patiently at the level crossing for an opportunity which never came to pass over the track. Nodding talking dolls with faces like Susan Hayward and June Allyson, and dolls houses and nurses outfits. Fretwork Sets and Carpentry Sets and games of draughts and ludo and Housey – Housey and giant paint boxes with every possible colour of paint, and a palette and an assortment of brushes. And, in the corner, the pride and joy and desire of every boy in Belfast. A number ten Meccano Outfit, with hundreds of red and green metal parts, rubber tyred wheels, brass gears, axles, nuts, bolts and spanners and screwdrivers. And a giant Meccano model of one of the Belfast trams which trundled past just now, complete with lights and turning wheels. A newsagents window overflowed with Christmas annuals – the *Dandy, Beano, Lion, Schoolfriend, Eagle, Girls Own, Radio Fun* and *Film Fun*, as well as *Picturegoer* and *Super Cinema Annual* and *Rupert the Bear*, and a very fine volume of *A Christmas Carol*, opened to show the illustration of Mr Scrooge embracing Tiny Tim. As I hurried along I was caught up in the wonderful cheery happy atmosphere abroad in the city tonight. How much laughter and joy and love filled each heart as all the people struggled homeward with all the treasures and parcels which would bring such happiness on the blessed Christmas morning. None would be excluded. Every heart would be merry and full on that day, for Christmas Day was the day of giving and sharing and bringing happiness to others.

I almost tripped over the old man. He lay sprawled on the footpath, right under my feet, just outside Queens Arcade. I glanced down at the thin unshaven face and the long matted hair on which the snow was sitting thickly and making the man look ridiculous. The man's jacket, ragged at the cuffs and torn at the pockets, wasn't much heavier than the collarless shirt he wore beneath it. I could see the wet snow had already seeped through his thin trousers. The sole of one of his shoes gaped open, wide, like a stranded fish's mouth. A few rolls of soggy Christmas wrapping paper, almost covered in snow, lay on the footpath beside him. A torn patch of brown cardboard tied around the old man's neck with a rough piece of string bore the barely legible information, scrawled in pencil: "Christmas paper. 1d. a sheet." No one looked at the old man. No one stopped. No one bought his Christmas paper. Not even at a penny a sheet.

"Paper. Christmas paper," he muttered, and I felt his eyes upon me. I stared down as the sad figure feebly lifted a roll of the sodden paper and held it toward me. But I too passed him by. I thought of giving him a few pennies. To get something to eat. He was probably hungry and I could see he was shivering from the bitter cold of the night. But giving him money would be a waste of time. And money as well. He wouldn't buy food. I knew he wouldn't. He was probably a drunk. He'd buy another bottle. Wine. Beer. Whatever. And he'd still be hungry, and even more drunk, drunk maybe to the point of unconsciousness. Lying in the snow on a night like this, drunk, he could freeze to death.

I walked on by. But not with an easy conscience. I crossed the street, slowly, dodging the trams and the occasional motor car looming out from the swirling blizzard of snowflakes. Safely on the other side I stopped and stared into McMullans bookshop window. McMullans was a good bookshop and I liked books. But I wasn't looking at the books. I was thinking. Thinking of the pathetic figure across the way. Thinking of the thin outstretched hand offering me Christmas paper for a penny a sheet. And the silent pleading in the eyes which looked not only into my own, but penetrated into the very depths of my heart, and found nothing there. I couldn't stop thinking of the old man. And remembering how I had walked straight past him, without even acknowledging his existence as he fixed me with those sad eyes. I turned away from the lighted bookshop window and stared across the street, trying to find the old man among all the people dashing past with their gaily wrapped parcels and packets through the fast-falling snowflakes. So many people! So much haste! So much to do! So little time! And I was in a hurry too. I had to get home to my own family who were waiting for me, warm and cheery around a blazing fireside and our Christmas tree with all the presents already beautifully wrapped for tomorrow. I certainly didn't need Christmas paper. But still I searched for the pitiful figure. I caught sight of him, half sitting, half lying on the snowy footpath. Why didn't he go home. It was Christmas Eve night. No one wanted his Christmas paper. No one needed it. Why didn't he just go home, wherever it was. At least he'd be warm there. Warm and dry. I stepped to the side of the kerb and waited for a snow-covered tram to groan by on its way toward York Street. When it passed I plunged back through the snow, towards Queens Arcade and the old man who was now almost indistinguishable from the sparkling white footpath on which he sat, head slumped low on his chest He didn't speak to anyone nor even attempt to offer up his soggy pieces of worthless Christmas paper. He didn't even raise his head as I drew near.

I stopped a few feet away from the shapeless form. Silently, and for a long time, I watched the rejected and dejected figure. Then, deliberately, I turned and walked away. I'd done what I could. I'd stopped and gone back. I had wanted to help. But he was asleep. Drunk. Like they all are. But there wasn't a bottle. That's what bothered me as I walked briskly along the street. There wasn't a bottle. A drunk usually has a bottle. Somewhere. In his hand. Raised to his lips. Sitting beside him. Rolling about in the gutter, drained and rejected, like the poor creature who'd sought to find solace in the empty promises it once offered.

The bottle is probably in his pocket, said a voice in my head. That's where it is. In his pocket. What does it matter where the bottle is, demanded another voice, the voice of conscience. Or if there's a bottle at all, or whether he's drunk or not drunk. He probably hasn't had food all day. Is it nothing to you, as you pass by, having everything, and needing nothing? Still I hesitated, not believing any few coppers I would give this man would go to nourish his body.

When the idea came to me it was so simple and so absolutely the right thing to do I couldn't believe I hadn't thought of it sooner. Buy some hot food. Put it straight into the old man's hand. That was the answer. Chips. Good old Belfast fish and chips! A big warm, well salted and vinegared fish supper, straight from the Mistletoe Cafe in High Street. That's what the man needed. A big fish supper.

You can't beat the thick folds of the Belfast Telegraph for wrapping up a fish supper. I felt the warmth of the fish and chips through the newspaper and smelt the vinegar as I pushed and shoved my way back along Donegal Place. Would the old man still be there? What if he'd had enough of the Christmas spirit? Or lack of it? Dragged himself to his feet and shuffled off to wherever he lived? No, I thought. Please. Please. Let him be there.

He was. Exactly as I'd left him. Asleep. Cautiously I moved toward the derelict figure. Now I wasn't so sure of myself. Not sure at all. I felt guilty, and presumptuous, and patronizing. Whatever his station in life, this poor creature would have his own dignity. What right had I to go thrusting a bag of chips into his face and by doing so let him know I considered him nothing more than a beggar looking for a handout? He might throw the food back in my face. And he'd have every right to do it.

But I was determined this old man would at least have the opportunity of a hot meal. He didn't even see me as I approached nor when I kneeled down beside him. Gently, very gently, I touched his shoulder. The old man's head came up immediately and I saw the panic in his eyes as he shrank back from my touch, and I feared I had made a bad mistake.

"I'm sorry," I murmured. "I didn't mean to disturb you, but – well – I've just bought these fish and chips and – and – well, there's too much for me. Do you think you could eat them?" I pushed the warm parcel into the thin bony hands and nodded reassuringly. The old man looked me straight in the eye. I knew he was assessing me. And my intentions. I waited for his decision.

A toothless smile broke out on the stubbled face. "I sure could," he answered, in a steady and grateful voice, and in a breath free from any hint of alcohol. " I surely could!"

I smiled, thankful I had achieved my mission with so little trouble and without the tirade of abuse I thought might come my way.

"What's your name," I asked, wondering at my own boldness as I did so. The man's name was none of my business and again I expected him to hurl the parcel of food into my face. But he didn't. He just stopped undoing the folds of the steaming newspaper and looked me straight in the eye once more.

"Deigo Joe," he replied. "That's what they call me. Diego Joe."

I nodded, appreciating this little confidence. I was about to ask how he came by such an unusual name, or if he'd ever been to San Diego. But I thought better of it. I learned the wisdom of this when in the next breath I asked Joe where he lived. His eyes flashed. Again I saw the fear, this time allied with anger and suspicion as he shrank back from me.

"I don't live anywhere," he cried, in an almost tearful voice. "Not in a house anyway. I sleep rough. But I'm not tellin' you where I sleep. I did tell somebody. Once. And they came in the night an' – an' – hit me, and took my blanket and what grub I had. I don't tell nobody where I sleep. An' I'm not tellin' you!"

I had pushed too far. I was about to move away when Joe spoke again as he fumbled with the parcel of fish and chips.

"But I wasn't always on the road y'know. I came from a good

family. Out Dundonald way. But I was the black sheep. Always the black sheep. So I cut out. Left it all behind. Couldn't be bothered with it. It was better on the road. On the road you know who your real friends are." There was a hint of pride in his voice as he continued. "I've no money comin' in y'know. I don't draw the dole nor nothin' like that." This time I thought my question was a valid one. "But how do you eat, Joe?" I asked. "What do you do for food?"

Joe looked at me and grinned as if I had asked the most stupid question it was possible to ask. "Just what I'm doin' now," he answered, sinking his teeth into a huge lump of fish he had extracted from the newspaper. "Just what I'm doin' now."

I nodded slowly, like an obtuse pupil who had finally managed to grasp the meaning of a very basic lesson in the school of life. It's one thing to read and hear great words of truth and wisdom and humility and pay lip-service with a nod of the head to the veracity of them. It was quite another to see that truth and wisdom and humility being worked out right in front of me, in the gutter of a Belfast street on Christmas Eve. Here was a man entirely without means – a man who didn't ask anyone for anything – yet was sure he would never go hungry. I thought of the first verse of the twenty-third psalm and I realized the hand which fed Joe at this moment was not mine, but that of another. But, still not having fully learned the lesson, I made another mistake as I tried, foolishly, to align myself with Joe's worldly poverty. "Life's not easy, Joe," I said. "Sometimes, when I've paid the mortage for my house, and the payment on the car, and looked after my family, there isn't very much left."

Joe picked up a chip. He studied it closely, then slipped it into his mouth. With a greasy hand he wiped his chin and smiled. To this very day I'm certain Joe was sympathizing for me as he uttered the last words I ever heard him speak.

"I don't have a house," he said, munching happily . "I don't have a motor car. I don't have a family. And I don't have any worries. Y'see, I'm content. With nothin'." I have never forgotten

Joe's words. I never will. They rang in my ears as I said goodbye to the old man and walked away from him that Christmas Eve night, humbled. And wiser. Much wiser.

The snow had stopped. Belfast lay white and silent beneath a starry sky and a gleaming brass moon. I looked back, to wave goodbye to Diego Joe. But I had already passed from Joe's life. I watched him finish the remains of his fish 'n chips. He wiped his mouth with the sodden cuff of his jacket. Then he raised a roll of the Christmas paper and I saw him mouth the words to the last of the last of the Christmas shoppers.

"Christmas paper. Penny a sheet."

No one looked at Joe. No one stopped. The spirit of Christmas walked on by.

The Happiest Christmas of All

I will always remember that Christmas. Always. As long as I live it will remain in my heart and in my memory as the happiest Christmas of all, a time of warmth and joy and happiness, when all things were wonderful, and all things were new.

But why, as I trudge along the streets of Belfast on this snowy Christmas Eve, why is the memory of that Christmas even more poignant now than in previous times? I have seen many Christmases come and go since that one, and been blessed by them all. But never has my spirit been moved and my heart warmed within me as it is tonight.

Perhaps it is the snow. It hasn't snowed on Christmas Eve for many years. But it is snowing now, and as the flakes fall thickly and encompass me in a swirling whiteness, so the memories of a Christmas past wrap themselves around me, and my step is lighter now than it has been for many a long year.

I like the snow, though it chills my bones. The snow is cold and clean and falls heaviest, as it did on that night, around the halo of light at the very top of the lamp post. I know this is an illusion. Even so I fasten my gaze on one of the swirling flakes and try to follow it as it spirals on its downward journey, just as I did all those years ago. It twists and turns, first this way, then that, teasing me as it seeks to hide among its fellows. I try to follow the dance of the snowflake. But I cannot, even as I could not when my eye was brighter and keener than it is now. I know the snowflake has fallen to the ground. But I do not know where.

The strains of Silent Night sung by the carollers around the Christmas tree at the city hall cause me to lift my head from the whiteness at my feet. I stop. I look. I listen, remembering how it was on that night. The words of joy and peace are sung softly. Reverently. They draw a wetness from my eyes to my cheeks. No one notices. Even if they do, they will attribute it to the melting of the snow upon my face.

I walk forward eagerly toward the Christmas tree and the lights and the carol singers. Suddenly I am no longer an old man walking alone in a Belfast street on Christmas Eve night. I am a little boy again – a little boy whose eyes are filled with wonder and excitement at the spectacle. How wonderful the tree is! How magnificent! And how many lighted lanterns splash red and green and pink and blue against its snowy branches! Balloons – giant balloons – and all the parcels wrapped in Christmas paper with the holly and the ivy and Santa Claus and his reindeer and snowmen with coal button coats and little black hats just like Stan and Ollie.

"Look! Look at the tree," I shouted to my father. "Did you ever see a Christmas tree as big as that? Did you? Did you ever?"

My father smiled and tousled my snowy wet hair and said he never had and that was why he had especially brought us in to the city from our country home this evening. He swept my little sister Molly up in his arms, just like a little doll, and perched her on his big broad shoulders. I shall never forget the excitement dancing in my sister's clear blue eyes as my father held her aloft and pointed to the top of the tree.

"Can you see it, Molly? Can you see what's on the very top of the tree?"

I'll always remember the smile, the great big smile of delight and joy as Molly flung her arms around my father's neck and hugged him tightly.

"A Fairy," she whispered shyly. "A Magic Fairy."

My father tightened Molly's little pixie-hat about her ears and kissed her cold nose. "That's right," he smiled. "A Fairy. A Magic Fairy. And on Christmas Eve everything is magical because this is the night our dear Saviour was born."

I stared up at the Magic Fairy as the snow fell upon my cheeks and stung my eyes and I wondered if it had been snowing the night the wise men came to the stable, and how sad it was there hadn't been any room at the inn. And I wondered if we would see the angels in the fields tonight when we stepped down from the bus and made our way to the little cottage on the hillside. The angels might appear to us, just as they had to the shepherds. And they might all come to our cowshed. They might. We had only one milking cow, Bluebell, so there would be plenty of room.

I felt my father's hand pressing gently on my shoulder. "Sing," he said. "Sing along with the carol singers. You know the words." He kissed my sister again on the tip of her nose and rubbed her apple-red cheeks with his knuckles. "And so do you Missy. You know the words. Don't you? Let's all sing *Silent Night.*"

And we did. Molly. And my father. And me. And all the great crowd of people, and all the carol singers in their winter coats and long woollen scarves which trailed in the snow, their faces shining from the glow of the candle-lit lanterns they held aloft. It was beautiful. Truly, it was a silent night. A holy night.

We sang *The First Noel* and *Good King Wenceslas* and *Away in a Manger* and then my father said as a special treat we could have one last look at the shops before we caught the bus back home.

The shops were closed at this late hour, but we didn't mind. Molly and I pressed our faces against the coldness of the brightly lit windows and gasped with delight at the treasures which lay so near and yet so far away on the other side of the glass.

One window was decorated with red and silver tinsel and twinkling fairy lights which blinked on and off. I wished we had fairy lights for our Christmas tree at home. But you needed electricity for fairy lights. The window was crammed with Santas and toy motor cars and boxes of games and walking-talking dolls and a train set you never needed to wind up. My father said someday, when we were richer, and if we had electricity, he would buy me a train set just like it. But this year my present would be a book. A very special book. And Molly would have her doll. Not the one that said "Mama" and "Papa". But maybe next year she could have that one. Maybe next year.

It wasn't snowing when we stepped down from the bus in the depths of the countryside, far away from the city. A pale moon hung in the jewelled sky and as far as I could see, all around me, in every direction, there was nothing but a stillness of white. Not a sound. Not a movement. My eyes roamed the vastness of the starry heavens, searching. But there were no angels, no shepherds in the fields. There wasn't anything in the fields, and there wasn't anything or anyone anywhere. Just Molly. And my father. And me, slipping and sliding and laughing our way home on a magical Christmas Eve night. I ran across the yard when we arrived home and opened the door of the cowshed. There wasn't anyone there. Only Bluebell, chewing contentedly. Still, it was a long night, and my father said Christmas Eve was a magical night. Anything could happen before morning. I went out and closed the door. But I didn't bolt it. The bolt on our cowshed door didn't fit very well and it was difficult to open. It would be even more difficult for angels and people who had travelled a long way and who didn't know how to work it. I didn't bolt the door.

I couldn't sleep that night. But it wasn't the cold that kept me awake. It was the excitement of the day gone and the day to come. It was the snow and the Christmas tree and the fairy lights and the carol singers and the Magic Fairy, and train sets you never needed to wind up, and angels and shepherds and wise men. And the apple and the orange and silver shilling I'd find in my stocking hanging at the bottom of my bed in the morning. And the book. Most of all it was the book my father had promised me for Christmas. My father said it was a very good book and it was written by a very famous man named Charles Dickens. My father said Mr Dickens was the best writer there ever was.

I was awakened on Christmas morning by my little sister imploring me to say hello to her new doll with the pink dress and bow my mother had made for it. Molly also got her apple and orange and silver shilling and a paint box and a colouring book. But Molly loved her doll best of all and immediately declared she would call it Annie, after our sister who had gone to be with the angels, and from now on the dolly would be Annie and she would look after her so she would never be sick again and wouldn't have to go away with the angels. I saw my mother glance up quickly at my father, then bow her head and turn away.

I got my orange and apple and silver shilling. But best of all I got my book. I pressed my fingers into the rich red binding and picked out the gold letters on the spine.

"*A Christmas Carol,*" I breathed, almost reverently. "By Charles Dickens."

"It's a good book," smiled my father, pleased I was pleased. "It's a Christmas story. Sometimes happy. Sometimes sad. But it has a joyful ending, and the moral of it is we should always try to help those who are less fortunate than ourselves." My father took the book from me and laid it on the chair beside him. He leaned forward and put his arm around my shoulder, fixing me with his steady gaze. "My boy, if a man has one true friend in the world, and a kindly heart, and the companionship of good books around him, that man is rich indeed. And if he possesses only the kindly heart, well then, he can bestow much riches on many people. Do you understand that?"

I nodded my head, not quite sure I did.

"Come then," laughed my father, rising up. "Help me kindle the fire and after breakfast I shall read to you from *A Christmas Carol*."

My mother smiled from the kitchen doorway as we carried in the kindling wood and the logs.

"Pile them high!" exclaimed my father. "Let no expense be spared. Today we shall have the warmest and cosiest cottage in all the countryside!"

On that Christmas Day we must surely indeed have had the warmest and cosiest little home in all the land. And after breakfast as my mother busied herself with the Christmas feast, my father pulled his chair up to the roaring blaze and set Molly on his knee.

"Come," he smiled to me. "Bring me your book and I shall read you a tale of long ago when a man's icy heart was so melted with love he did nothing but good to everyone he met for the rest of his days."

Joyfully I handed the book to my father and drew my stool up beside him. He cradled Molly in his arms and carefully opened the volume. He turned the first page and glanced at it. Then he stared me straight in the eye, looking over the top of his spectacles. "To begin with," he said, "Joseph Marley was dead."

What a story that was! Christmas Eve and ghosts in clanking chains and a hard old miser named Ebeneezer Scrooge. How we laughed at Mr Fessiwig and shed tears over Tiny Tim and by the time old Scrooge's heart was finally melted it was time for our own Christmas dinner.

"It WAS a turkey!" exclaimed my father quoting from the book he'd just read and standing poised ready to carve our own bird. We couldn't afford a big turkey. Not this year. But what did that matter said my father. We had each other. And with this we all heartily agreed.

The angels didn't come to our cowshed that Christmas. The wise men didn't come either, or if they did they'd gone long before I remembered to go out to look for them. But for me, it was the happiest – the happiest – Christmas of all.

Now, all these years later, I stand alone among the crowds beneath the Christmas tree at the City Hall. The dampness of the snow eats into my weary bones. But I hear the singing of the carols and my heart is warmed within me as I remember that Christmas of years gone. My gaze travels slowly to the top of the tree. There is the Magic Fairy. But my mother and father have long since gone to be with the angels and I have not seen my sister Molly for many years and I think she will never see me again.

But you, dear friend. Perhaps you will see me on the streets. Tonight. When you bring your children to see the Christmas tree. Our paths might cross in the city centre, or in any town, or in any village across the land. Not understanding, your children will clutch your hand even more tightly when they see me. And because you do not understand, you will draw them even closer to the safety of your side. I do not mind that you turn your face and avoid me. I am saddened. Perhaps hurt. But that pain is for me to bear. I mean no harm to you or your children. But sometimes, sometimes I wonder what thoughts go through your mind as you avert your gaze from mine. Do you think I am about to beg coppers from you? Do you look upon my rough and ragged clothing and dismiss me as a beggar, a thief, a down and out? I beg from no-one, nor yet do I steal. Perhaps I am down, for life has dealt harshly with me. And I am sorry if I have embarrassed you because you have misjudged my intentions or are offended by my rough dress.

But you are looking upon things which are external, not those which are within the heart, and which are the true measure of a man. Even so, it grieves me if I have given you or your little ones cause for concern. It would never be in my heart to do such a thing.

Now the snow falls heavier, the night is colder. I take a last lingering look at the Christmas tree and the lights and the Magic Fairy. Then I turn away to seek a little shelter. I know not where I will lay my head tonight, nor what, if anything, I will eat tomorrow. But tonight I will sleep and dream of angels and wise men and the Ghost of Christmas to Come, when Want and Poverty and Sorrow will indeed be a thing of the past.

And to you, dear friend, and to all those you hold more precious than life itself, I wish you the happiest of all happy Christmases. And may the memory of it live on in your heart, long after the day itself, is done.

The Little Boy and The Old Man

It happened long, long ago, on a certain Christmas Eve night. I lay as quiet as a mouse in my little bed, as all little boys should on the night before Christmas. But I was not asleep, and did not intend to sleep, even if I had been able to overcome the excitement which reigned within me. I lay back on my pillow and gazed through the icy window pane of my bedroom. I gazed in wonderment at the pale moon hanging in the silent star-spangled sky. My eyes explored the heavens, to the twinkling blue stars, and away beyond them, seeking for the one who would travel the circumference of the whole world before this night was over, bringing joy and happiness to children everywhere.

It was a perfect Christmas Eve night. The fields and hills beyond my window lay silent and still under the fall of new clean snow which sparkled icy white. The silvery moon gleamed like a new sixpence, lighting the entire countryside as clear as day. I couldn't hear a sound. All the world was wrapped in silence – a strange, mystical silence. The silence, and the snow, and the expectation of what was about to happen made this a magical Christmas Eve night, a night such as I had never experienced before. Magic was indeed abroad tonight. I could sense it, I could feel it all around me, the power and the closeness of it so real it reached into my innermost being, deep inside me. So powerful and intense was the feeling I felt I could reach out and touch it.

It would happen tonight. I knew it would. This would be the night I would meet the old gentleman. I had longed to meet him for a very long time – the jolly old man who was the friend of children everywhere – the one who was the very epitome of goodness and truth and kindness and generosity. I pondered again in my mind the question to which no one had ever been able to give me a satisfactory answer. Why was it nobody had ever seen this kind old gentleman? Every Christmas it was the same. He arrived, late on Christmas Eve night or early on Christmas morning, bestowed all the wonderful gifts on the children, and was gone, without ever making himself known. That was the most beautiful thing about him – he gave to everyone, yet didn't wait to be thanked. No one knew the old gentleman's age, for I had enquired about this many times. But he was very old. And very wise. He knew everything there was to know about everything and everybody, without anyone having to tell him. How I hoped I might meet him tonight. Just this one time. To say "thank you". Many a Christmas Eve I had snuggled into my bed, determined I would not succumb to the shades of sweet sleep until I greeted the old man and thanked him as he entered my bedroom. But always I had failed. The old man was patient. Very patient. Each Christmas Eve he waited. And waited. And waited. He waited for just that instant when I closed my eyes – not to sleep – but just to rest them for a moment – and then it was all over. He sprinkled stardust and when I awoke it was Christmas morning. The old gentleman was gone, leaving behind all the joy and blessings of his visit. I had failed again.

It would be different this Christmas. I was wide awake, my thoughts and senses as clear as the starlit sky beyond my window-pane. I could stay awake for just as long as it took. I hugged the blankets closer around my neck and wriggled my toes at the foot of the cold bed. I fixed my eyes on the pale white moon. This could be a long night. A very long night. But I didn't mind. I was fully prepared. Everything was ready. Everything was perfect. I knew, beyond any shadow of doubt, this would be the night when I finally saw the old man arrive. It would be tonight.

I didn't see him come into the room. I didn't hear him. But suddenly, without a sound – without a movement – he was there – the old man – sitting on the side of my bed, his cheery round face smiling into mine. I wasn't afraid, or startled, or anxious. Nor did I call out to alert the rest of the household. I was aware, instantly, the old man had come to see me, and only me. I was warm and comfortable and perfectly at ease and filled with an overwhelming sense of joy in the old man's presence. And I knew that even if I did call for the rest of the household they wouldn't be able to see the old gentleman. He had come to visit me, and me alone, to fulfil my childhood dream.

I turned my head on the pillow and gazed upon the kindly face and twinkling blue eyes. I knew a smile was playing about the lips behind the snow-white whiskers. The old gentleman wasn't dressed as I thought he would, but my heart overflowed with happiness he should make himself known to me – a little nobody, not even eight years old – in a tiny cottage, in a tiny field, in the depths of the snow-covered countryside. My visitor's presence seemed to fill the room with love and kindness and goodwill, and a warmth and soft glow I could feel despite the coldness of the night.

But now, in spite of all the wonderful declarations I had determined to make known to the old man when I met him, my lips were silent. I was in awe. What should I say to this dear kind person I had wanted to meet for such a long, long time? What words should I speak? Would he want to hear me?

But it was the old man who spoke first. "Good evening, little boy," he murmured as he pushed my tousled hair away from my now even more wide awake eyes. "Is everything well with you on this beautiful Christmas Eve?"

I smiled, a little smile, encouraged by the rich warmth and sincerity of the old man's deep voice.

"Yes, thank you sir," I replied. "I am very well. And I hope you are too?"

The old man nodded, blue eyes sparkling. "I too am very well," he answered. "And very pleased to be with you tonight. I believe you have desired - for a very long time - to meet with me?"

"Indeed I have sir," I whispered, thinking of the long and cold journey the old man had already made and how much farther he had yet to travel before the night was over. "I have waited many years to see you. But I know you are very busy and have so little time to do so much work in a single night. Please sir? How do you manage to do it? How do you travel around the whole world in so little time?"

The old man patted my arm gently, nodding his snow-white head as he listened to my question. Again I sensed the wise and kindly smile behind the soft downy whiskers.

"Time?" whispered the old man. "Time? Little boy, there are many things difficult for one so young to understand. Difficult even for those who have lived a lifetime of years to understand. But tonight, little boy, and for tonight only, you will have the mind of one who has lived, not for many years, but through all the ages. You will understand many words no child your age ever understood before. And if you keep these words in your heart you will be rich. Forever. Do you have an ear to hear, little boy?"

I snuggled even closer into the warmth of my blankets and nodded my head vigorously. The old man seemed to me to be the very fount of wisdom and knowledge and kindness and I waited expectantly for him to speak again.

"Firstly, little boy," he began, "there is no such thing as time. There is only now. You cannot return to what is passed. It is gone. Forever. It will not come back. Neither can you live for one moment in the future, for that is yet to be, and may never be.

The only time is now. Little boy, whatever good lies within your heart to do, or whatever noble achievements you hope to attain, seek to do them at the moment they enter your heart. Or at least begin the commencement of them. Now is the only time you can be certain of. Yesterday will be gone. Tomorrow may not be yours. Do you understand, little boy?"

I nodded. I fully grasped the deep depths of this wisdom. How I came to understand, I did not know. But I did. I opened my mouth to speak, then closed it again, fearing any words I should utter would be foolishness to the old man.

"Speak, little boy," encouraged the old man. "Do not be afraid. Speak the things which are within your heart."

"Old man," I whispered. "I know you are very old. And very wise. Please sir, why does the darkness always come at night? Why doesn't the sun shine all the time, for ever and ever, so there is no night. Wouldn't that be better than darkness?"

The old man turned and motioned to the window on the far side of the room. "Look, little boy. Look through the window pane. What do you see?"

I gazed through the window, staring up into the very depths of the Christmas Eve night sky.

"I see the moon," I answered. "Shining brightly. And I see the stars. Hundreds, thousands of stars, twinkling brightly."

"You do indeed," laughed the old man. "And how beautifully they shine tonight, filling the heavens with the glory of their splendour. How privileged we are to behold them." He paused. "But, little boy, if the sun always shone in the sky, for ever and ever and ever, and there was no night, what would become of the moon and the stars?"

I immediately perceived the direction of the old man's thinking and the wisdom of it.

"Never again would we see the moon," I answered sadly. "Or the stars. It would be too bright. Much too bright."

"Indeed it would," agreed the old man as he pointed to the sky and its gleaming jewels. "The beauty of the moon and stars would be lost to us. Forever. Never again would we gaze upon their glory. Would you desire that, little boy?"

I shook my head slowly, and I knew the old man understood what was in my heart.

"You see, little boy," said the old man. "In life we are often blessed with many bright and joyful times. But sometimes there comes a darkness. Happiness and the joy of life departs from us. But little boy, this is only for a season. The darkness will bring forth it's own light, revealing unto you a deeper understanding of things you never knew before. You will see light shining in the darkness, just as the night sky brings forth the glory and light of the moon and stars."

I stared again at the moonlit sky, and the boundlessness of the starry heavens.

"Old man," I asked, "how can you fly around the world, not having wings?"

The old man smiled. He shook his head. "Little boy," he murmured, "I cannot fly. The birds of the forest are born to take wing and fly through the heavens. And so they should. But not I. I am always close to the earth, in my walk, and in my way of life. Many seek to reach great heights, perhaps of power and wealth and fame, for which they are not fitted. Often they will sell character and name to rise higher than their fellows for a passing earthly glory. It reveals a heart which lacks contentment and peace and humility. Do you understand, little boy?"

"I do indeed sir," I replied, without hesitation. It seemed to me I could understand everything, even all the mysteries of the world and the universe and ages gone and ages which might yet come, and all by just listening to the gentle soft words of the old man.

"Well," continued my visitor, "dream your dreams, little boy. Seek to do great things if you will. But not in vanity, nor pride, nor arrogance. Hurt no-one. Let your word be your bond. Sell neither character nor reputation, not for all the treasures in the world, for they are precious, and beyond price. Once lost, they can never be restored. They are gone. Forever. If you remember nothing else of what we speak tonight, little boy, remember this. Be honourable in all things."

I promised my night time visitor I would remember, not only this, but every word he spoke to me. Then, growing bolder, I put another question.

"Old man," I said. "Where do you live? Is it far, far away?"

This time the old man paused and was slow to reply. "No, little boy," he whispered. "Not far. Very near. Like the spirit of Christmas itself, I live within the hearts of men and women and boys and girls all over the world. So you see, I live everywhere, in every heart that is open to me. I am very close to everyone."

The wise words of the old man swam about in my brain and I longed to hear more of such wisdom and kindness as I had never heard before. But my eyes were growing heavy, and the old man sensed it.

"Little boy," he whispered softly. "You and I must soon take our leave, one from the other. We will never meet again. I wish you well, little boy, now on this blessed Christmas Eve night, and throughout all life's journey. May you know much brightness and joy and happiness. But always remember, even in the dark times of testing, there will come forth the bright light of comfort and wisdom and compassion which will reveal unto your heart true riches, that you may be a blessing to others. In all things, little boy, keep a good heart."

I nodded my head sleepily. "Please. Please, old man. Say you will come back again." The old man shook his head slowly. "I hope I shall always be with you, little boy," he murmured, "forever, though you will never see me again. Remember this night, and the words we have shared together. Speak softly as you go through life. And always, in the true spirit of Christmas, be ever ready to stretch out your hand to help another. A word of comfort, a cup of cold water where it is needed, for there is much need and too few to give the ease of it. Remember these things, little boy, and you will be much blessed."

As the old man's words floated softly around me and deep down into the recesses of my mind and young heart, I hardly knew if I was awake or asleep. But happiness and joy and peace were all around me as I listened to the warm gentleness of the old man's kind voice. Now I could barely discern one word from another. All the words were connecting, weaving together to make a golden tapestry of the most beautiful sounds I had ever heard. The sounds carried me up, up and away, away from my little bed and my little bedroom and I was not afraid, up into the heavens, past the gleaming golden moon, away beyond the stars which shone with such brightness as I had never seen, to a place I saw not with my eyes, but with my spirit, and where I longed to be forever, and ever, and ever...

Now I sit alone on this Christmas Eve night, far, far, removed from that Christmas Eve of so long ago. I am no longer a little boy. I sit in the near darkness in front of my cheery fireside and it is with the eyes of age I look back and reflect upon life and its mysteries. The blazing yuletide logs crackle and spit filling the room with warmth and comfort. And memories. Precious memories. I observe, as I used to observe in days of childhood, pictures of people and places and things, taking shape in the glowing fire. As the fire burns brightly the pictures alter. As in life they change, slowly but surely, from one thing into another, then alter again to form yet another new image. Silently, I watch the pictures come and go. My mind wanders back in time, across the years, to that blessed Christmas Eve and the old man who came to visit me and talk with me in the night-time. Who was he? Was there really an old man? Or was he just the night time dream of a young mind excited with the promises of the Christmas Day to come? And yet, as I have asked myself many times, how could a young child with a mind unformed in the ways of the world and its truths and its deceits, dream dreams with such depths of wisdom and knowledge? For many years, on many Christmases, I have pondered the question over and over again. I am no nearer an answer now than I was in the beginning. But I have lived long enough to know there are indeed "more things in heaven and earth, than are dreamt of in our philosophy." The wise words which came to me from the old gentleman on that night have remained with me. Always. Many times they have been a comfort and blessing to me, when blessing and comfort seemed far way.

And now, on this Christmas Eve night, many a little head will rest upon a quiet pillow, knowing nothing of life's trials, but only of the joy and wonder and expectation of that one who will come in the night time when all the world is at rest, to fill hearts with joy and happiness on the morrow. And it may be that tonight you will be the one chosen to be the fount of wisdom and kindness, charged by the duty of love, to visit and guide a little one in the true direction along life's pathway. It may be that amidst the excitement of Christmas you will be the one to reveal the true spirit of this blessed season. Yours are the words which will be remembered, now, and in all the years to come, and used to shape a young life to all that is honourable and noble and good. And the words of wisdom and love will live on. And when the little one with whom you speak becomes full of years, he or she may speak to another little one, who in turn will become aged and old, and who again will speak the words of wisdom and truth. Truly, as the old man said, there will be no such thing as time. Only the blessed spirit of Christmas, living on, for ever, and ever, and ever. In heaven. And in earth…

Long Ago and Far Away

Last night I saw the harvest moon. It reminded me of childhood, a childhood of long ago and far away. For a long time I observed the silent silvery orb hanging gracefully in the peaceful sky. I remembered other times and other days. I remembered the autumns of my country childhood.

Even as a child I could tell exactly when autumn arrived. It wasn't always on the same date. But there came a morning which announced itself with a distinct coolness, a heavy dew upon the fields, a quietness in the air, hedgerows quivering with ghostly spiders webs glistening liquid gold as the sun, not as strong as he had been in summer, began his weary climb.

Autumn brought me, with not a little regret, to the end of my summer holidays. It was time to return to the old schoolhouse – Ballyvester School – near Donaghadee. It was the end of one time and the beginning of another – new teacher, new books, new pencils, and a determination to do much better in the autumn season than I had in the previous.

We walked to school. That was a lesson in itself. As droves of us ambled playfully down the Ballyhay Road the autumnal countryside all around provided ample evidence of the new season which had drifted in almost imperceptibly on the wings of dying summer. The blackberry briars, heavy with plump juicy fruit, ran rampant through the high hawthorn hedges, providing us with a late addition to our hastily gulped breakfast and a more leisurely feast on the way home. It always seemed to take twice as long to come home from school as it did to get there. Maybe that's because in addition to feasting upon blackberries there were orchards to raid and hungry stomachs to fill with apples and pears and gooseberries and even long crisp carrots which grew abundantly in the fields alongside the road. On the way to school we eyed the corn-stooks and the haystacks and the half dug potato fields. There was more work to be done when school was over. But for now it was the old schoolroom which beckoned us.

We were a typical country school. I don't believe any of us had any higher ambition in life than to plough a field or milk a cow. Book-work and lessons simply got in the way of all that and it wasn't unknown for some fortunate pupil to be kept from his desk because he was needed on the land at harvest time. But we always enjoyed that morning when we returned to the old place for the new term. I loved the smell of the new pencils as they were handed out by Mrs Donaldson – the thickness of the new reading book, and the new wooden ruler as yet free from inkstains and perfectly straight edged and uncarved by pen-knife of the finest Sheffield steel. Even the jotters, whose pages had the absorbent texture of toilet-paper, were bright and inviting, offering the opportunity for a new start, good work and good marks.

Our composition books enjoyed a better class of paper. At the beginning of each autumn term I resolved my hand-writing would now be majestic and the envy of the entire class. The new composition book deserved no less. On the first day of the new term, on the first page, my efforts were herculean. In retrospect I suppose my offerings could be called, at best, tidy. But as each autumn day slipped past and the leaves on the hedgerows outside rusted and decayed and fell away, so did the quality of my mediocre writing upon the pages. Before October passed my resolve was broken, my good intentions blown down in the wind like the leaves of sycamore and ash and beech which rustled among our feet on our daily treks to the place of learning.

We did sums at our school. We'd never heard of maths. I hated sums. I couldn't do them and had no aptitude for them. But, as with the new composition book and the hand-writing, I somehow imagined a new book for sums, neatly ruled and margined with my new ruler and pen would somehow offset the dullness of my brain and work wonders for my talents in the adding up, subtracting and long division game.

It was a forlorn hope. With every bold red cross entered against my finished calculations the neatness of my faulty work went into a rapid decline at twice the speed of the composition book work. In a few weeks the entire class was in the same boat – ragged paged jotters, ink-stained essays, rulers carved into offensive and defensive weapons and our steel nibbed pens daggers with which to carve our initials in the old wooden desks. School wasn't for us. And especially not in autumn when there was still work to be done in the fields.

How carefree and happy were those childhood autumn days when school was out. There was still the remainder of the harvest to be brought in. All summer we had sweated in the corn-fields, following Robert Strain and the binder, gathering up the sheaves of golden corn and stooking them to further ripen in the hot blazing sun. We'd built the haystacks in the fields of sweet red and purple clover, working from sun-up until sun-down, ensuring all would be safe before the onset of winter winds and rains. All was a flurry of work and ceaseless activity and the shouting of men and barking of dogs and birds warbling in the hedges and a relentless sun beating down. And yet, on the first night of the harvest moon, I walked alone through the same fields, wondering at the gentle mystical scene all around me. The fields lay silent under the moon's silvery light. The ghostly brightness struck eveything dumb, and everything motionless, the exact opposite of what happened when the burning sun ruled the firmament. The corn-stooks bowed their heads, as if in silent worship, and the haystacks cast their bulky shadows across the stubbled meadow. The silent moon ruled the starlit sky, the earth, and all its inhabitants. It seemed impossible man had played any part in the beauty of the harvest night lying before me, and even less that I should have contributed to it in any way. I walked slowly among the corn-stooks. Touching. Reverently, gently, I touched each bowed head of golden grain given up by the earth for the use of man. And in the touching, I received my blessing.

Those early autumn days just after school got out, were happy days. We could steal a ride on the ruck-shifter as Robert Strain and his son Raymond hauled the haystacks from the fields to the safety of the stackyard. We clung to the stack on the ruck-shifter as best we could and bounced across the field and down the dusty road. Ah! To be a child again. And ride the ruck-shifter.

We dug the potatoes. The smell of the rich black soil filled my nostrils and I could almost taste the saltiness of the rich white harvest we gathered from the giving earth. The fine peaty soil always gave an abundant crop – more than enough to see us all through the long winter. It was good to be part of the harvest. And to bring the harvest home.

We picked blackberries. Droves of us again, boys and girls, straggled out along the lanes and lonens and around the perimeter of the fields which had so lately given up their own provision of rich booty. We carried the blackberries in shiny tin milk-cans, buckets, basins, wicker-baskets and even meal bags and filled them to overflowing as we hunted among the ripping thorns of the briars for more and more of the plump treasures secreting themselves amidst the nettles and gorse. We gorged ourselves as we tramped from hedge to hedge and field to field, and there was still more than enough to carry home to make pots of bramble jelly. Our fingers were torn and ripped and stained and our blood mingled freely with the purple juice of the berries. We hardly noticed. This wasn't work or hardship. It was part of our play.

And soon we'd enjoy the rich red jam on a farl or two of home made soda or wheaten bread, warm, and not long off the griddle. I never see children in the lonens now, hunting the blackberries. And who knows how to use a griddle, or strain the juice of the berries in a muslin cloth? But in my memory I can still taste the sweet creamy froth from the jam as it bubbled in the pot on the old stove and I can still see my grandmother sipping and tasting, sipping and tasting, until it was just right for cooling and bottling.

Well, maybe I should confess. Perhaps it's not all memory. Every autumn evening, before the sun finally sinks low in the stubbled fields, one figure even yet haunts the hedgerows, gathering the precious harvest. I have seen many summers. And many autumns. Yet, like a child, I still wander the old roads, like one returning home, gathering blackberries, as I did in days of childhood. Now it is my wife Betty who stirs the jam and revives memories of days that used to be.

When the hedgerows have given up their last berry and the jams are safely stored and the swallows ready themselves for the journey which must come soon, the nights darken quickly. The setting sun, sensing the battle is lost, makes a last valiant show before he dies in the western sky. The sun is bigger than I have ever seen it – almost huge – a dying crimson ball slipping down and away from its position of once mighty power. The autumn leaves, bronze and gold, hurry along the deserted pathways, seeking their final place of rest. But the sweet scents of honeysuckle and over ripe apples hang yet in the evening air as the rising harvest moon usurps the defeated sun and claims her throne in the night sky. The swallows – hundreds of them – prepare themselves on the telegraph wires for their journey. It is almost time. Time for Halloween.

Halloween! A time for fireworks and ghost-stories around the fire. Witches abroad on their broomsticks, monkey-nuts and apple-tarts and apple-ducking. And of course Halloween rhyming and the old verse we knew so well:–

Halloween is coming and the goose is getting fat,
Please put a penny in the old man's hat
If you haven't got a penny, a hapney will do.
If you haven't got a hapney, God bless you!

The Halloween rhyming was vitally important to us children in the nineteen forties and nineteen fifties. Pennies were hard to come by. The coppers we'd earned by our toil in the harvest fields had long since been spent on ice-cream and bags of dulse and the occasional trip out to the Copeland Islands on the motor-boats The Miss Dorothy or The White Heather. Now we needed fireworks for the big night on the thirty-first of October. And the only way to secure the finances required was by Halloween rhyming.

From farmhouse and humble cottage we trekked off around the back roads and lonens, our faces well concealed behind fear-some Halloween masks if we could afford them, or blacked up like Al Jolson with soot or boot-polish if we couldn't. I don't know why we needed to keep our identity a secret. But we always did. Maybe it made it easier to call to the same house the second or even a third time in the hope of another donation to supple-ment the coffers.

We pulled turnips from the field and carved them with our pen-knives, hollowing out the most horrible and ghastly features our young minds could imagine. When we inserted the candle on a pitch-black night they would be even more terrifying. Then, with lanterns lit, wrapped up and blacked up, with stout hearts and shining faces we set off into the darkness to do the rhyming.

We didn't have any sense of time on those long ago nights. We wandered all over the countryside, across fields and up long stony lonens to visit farmhouses sometimes half a mile apart. Ballyhay and Killaughey, Ballyfotherley and Ballycopeland and even on down into Hoggstown. We journeyed to every townland we could reach in the travels of a night. We were all noise and bravado and derring do as we trudged along, breathing in the sweet night air. But there was much shoving and pushing and trying to get to the rear of the gathered assembly, and much less bravado, when we reached the first lamp-lit cottage and it was time to knock upon the door and commence the rhyming. And especially if the house belonged to some hard faced old cratur we were afraid to meet in broad daylight, never mind in the pitch dark. The youngest of our entourage was thrust to the front. The best and brightest turnip-lantern was thrust into his arms. We knocked on the door as loudly as we dared and instructed our young companion to "sing up!"

Only rarely did we come away from a door empty handed. Usually it was a few hapney's or pennies we took in the battered hat we held out more in hope than expectation. But sometimes thruppeny-bits and even shiny sixpences glinted in the candle-light. Once I discovered a whole silver shilling among the coppers. Never a two shilling piece, or a half-crown.

We were honourable Halloween rhymers. We didn't waste our hard won gain on sweets or crisps or ice-cream. Every penny we took was spent on fireworks from John McGuffin's shop in Donaghadee. What an assortment John had! The Mighty Atom. Catherine Wheels. Jumping Jennies. The Thundercrack. Rockets and Roman Candles and much, much more. And though we were sorely tempted, not one of the blue touchpapers was lit before Halloween Night.

There was usually a bit of harmless mischief done about the countryside before we enjoyed the spectacular dazzle and luminescence of the exploding fireworks. Ah! There was something mystical and magical in the very smell of the blue and red and purple sulphurous smoke drifting skyward in the fusion of light and dark and colour.

When the last rocket had fallen to earth we trudged into Mrs Strain's farmhouse. Now there was apple-ducking to enjoy. And Mrs Strain's home made apple-tart and short-bread and the fruits of her orchard – apples, pears and plums. Ghost stories by the dim light of the oil-lamp, more to eat and drink and when it was all over the long trudge through dark fields to our own homes, and not without a few furtive looks over our shoulder at some ghostly apparition we sensed might be following us.

There was much to be grateful for in gentle autumn. Not least the harvest, safely gathered in. Every Sunday morning my little sister Ann and I attended Shore Street Presbyterian church in Donaghadee, though not always with a great deal of enthusiasm. But how different it was for the Harvest Thanksgiving service! What joy to enter the doors, guarded on each side by long rows of stooked corn exactly the same as we'd worked in our own fields. Bouquets of honeysuckle and rambling rose, marigolds and meadowsweet and Lily of the Valley on the window ledges and hanging from the rafters. Mounds of home baked breads of every description and shape – rectangular, circular, triangular and oblong – adorning the communion table. Baskets of newly dug white potatoes lying in a bed of their own black peat soil. Cabbages and turnips and carrots and parsley and peas and beans and beetroot. Home made jams and fruit preserves and the full joy and knowledge that everything was safely gathered in and that we ourselves had played a little part in that great work. Our enthusiasm knew no bounds as we lustily sang the beautiful words of the old hymn "We plough the fields and scatter the good seed on the land. And it is fed and watered by God's own tender hand ..."

Autumn is still, even as it was in my childhood, a beautiful season – perhaps the fairest of them all. And it is indeed a time for thanksgiving. It is a time of rest, not only for the natural things we see around us, but also for ouselves as we reflect on times gone, pleasures enjoyed, labour diligently carried out, sorrows borne, wisdom, and hopefully, contentment attained. Let us enjoy the peace and tranquility of autumn. And as all is gathered in, let us each one be grateful for every blessing it brings to those with an ear to hear, an eye to see. And perhaps our memory will cause us once more to walk in those precious days of childhood, which are now so long ago, and far away.

Part II

A Travelling Man

Dream, that's the thing to do,
Dream and it could come true.

Popular Song

The Town of Books

There's a tiny town which has won my heart. Although its fame has spread world wide not many people know it, or its whereabouts. Pull your car over, even fifteen miles from Hay, and the locals will scratch their head as you enquire as to which direction it might lie in.

I don't consider myself a globe-trotter. True, I've managed to spend a little time in a few places I considered worth travelling to see - Paris, Versailles, London, Moscow, St. Petersburg - and even sunny California and old San Diego. Beautiful places. Some of them I've visited on more than one occasion. But I am distinctly miffed if a trip to any of these means I must forgo my annual pilgrimage to Hay-on-Wye. I am not happy. I must see Hay. At least once a year. I begin to resist and resent the glories of St. Petersburg and the big blue California sky. My heart yearns for Hay. And if I tell you that when I get to Hay I reside in a tiny tent in a field just outside the sleepy town, perhaps the uniquely Northern Ireland term "headbin" might spring easily to mind.

So. What draws me every year to Hay? Firstly, Hay is *not* Ballyhay, beloved townland of my childhood. Hay is in Wales. Well, most of it is. A tiny fraction of it – a handful of houses – struggled over the border into England. Find the town of Hereford and strike out toward the Black Mountains through miles and miles of isolated rural countryside. Eventually, with a bit of luck, you'll discover Hay. But that's not the way I travel to my favourite town. An old campaigner like me long ago discovered another route even more isolated and almost as secret as Hay itself. We come into Hay – my wife Betty and I – from Ross. It's all motorways and pretty decent roads through England as far as Ross. Then it's all B-roads. Hilly up and down dirt-tracks sneak past tumbledown cottages with wild and overgrown gardens full of statuesque hollyhocks and sprawling gold and scarlet nasturtiums. Rambling roses – white and pink and scarlet – claim the hedgerows with glorious pink mallow trees, and there always seems to be a farmer and his dog ambling through gleaming meadows of golden buttercups. Civilization, or what passes for it, is already far behind us. We are in the Golden Valley. And golden it is. The rising landscape on either side is a patchwork with sunlit fields of barley and wheat and corn shimmering in the summer sun. We are reminded of country childhood days and of a time that used to be. If you visit Hay, come by the Golden Valley.

But on our first attempt to find Hay we came by the other route, on the main road, or as near a main road as you can find to the little town, late on a wet, misty and dull afternoon. We came upon it so suddenly it took us by surprise. No suburbs. We just crested the brow of a hill and turned a sharp bend and there was tiny Hay nestling secretly in the valley just beneath us – a real live Brigadoon. We'd found it. Right in the middle of nowhere. I fell in love with it immediately.

But why had I made such a determined effort to come on this little place which even now after years of experience I can only find on the map with great difficulty. Well, I have always been a book-lover. All writers love books. But as far back as I can remember, in early childhood, I had a recurring dream where I suddenly discovered a little village hidden deep in a dark forest. It was a secret place and the village was filled with nothing but books. The citizens did nothing except write books, sell books and read books. Every single tumbledown shop was bursting with books. They crammed the windows, blocked the doorways and spilled out onto the dusty streets. Everyone had their nose stuck in a book and the conversation was only of books and nothing but books and the people were happy all the time and never needed to leave their little secret village. In years of travelling up and down the length and breadth of the U.K. I discovered that the best books were usually old books, long out of print and usually discovered in junk shops or the occasional second-hand bookshop one might stumble upon. Just before another of our camping trips on the mainland Betty presented me with a paperback which detailed the best second-hand bookshops in Britain. Among the dozens listed were shops right on our usual route – one in Carlisle, two in Stratford-upon Avon, one in Salisbury, two in Tewkesbury. And thirty-six in Hay. Hay? Where was Hay? I'd never heard of it. But apparently if it was a second-hand book you wanted – on any subject – Hay-on-Wye was the place to be. Hay, in the middle of nowhere, right on the English/Welsh border, a town with one chipshop, a people population of thirteen hundred - and a book population of a couple of million volumes. I had to find Hay – The Town Of Books.

Our camp site, Radnors End, was right on the top of the hill where we were now, overlooking the town. It's a lovely compact little site and much used and loved by the hill-walkers and climbers. The owners, Zena and Steve Davies, gave us a warm welcome – as they have every year since that first night – and made sure we were well settled in. But I couldn't wait to get down to Hay even though it was late in the evening before we'd secured our tent and made everything shipshape for our stay. I knew the shops would be closed. That didn't deter me. Heavy misty clouds covered Hay Bluff and the Black Mountains and swept right down to hide the roof-tops of Hay as we ambled down the hill in the rain and across the bridge over the River Wye to discover the late night pleasures the town had to offer.

Hay is small. Very small. Tiny hilly maze-like streets, where you seldom encounter a motor car, lead you round and round in circles. Even when you think you've traversed them all – and you can tramp them all in about fifteen minutes – there's always another little lane you seemed to have missed first time around in the nine hundred year old settlement. The town is dominated by Hay Castle, a rambling ruin standing at the head of the hill in Castle Street. Not distant nor protected, or barricaded up. You walk two minutes up the tiny twisting street past the stone clock to where the War Memorial stands and you're at the castle wall and a door which is conveniently never locked. At eight o'clock at night, with nobody about, we wondered if perhaps we could sneak a little look inside the grounds.

We did. I couldn't believe what I saw. An open grassy courtyard lay before me. Its four walls held rows and rows of metal bookcases, each about six feet high, and each crammed with books of every description. It was a fairy-tale in itself – thousands of books – a treasure trove of literary leaves, and nobody in attendance. I couldn't quite understand it. But I was in there immediately, devouring the contents and trying to make sense of why so many volumes were left completely unattended. I was to learn that's the way it is in Hay. No one locks their door. Shopkeepers hang up little scribbled notices on the front of their premises "Sorry – just nipped out. Come in. Have a look around. Won't be long." Truly, a step back in time.

It was Betty who spotted the Honesty Box, a slit like a post office box set into the stone wall with a little note which bore the information "Hardbacks 50 pence. Paperbacks 25 pence." You simply loaded up with the literary treasures of your choice, at give-away prices, and dropped the money into the box. If you'd been a mean-spirited character, which no true booklover ever is, you could have walked off with a mountain of books. For free.

That was the night we discovered The Three Tuns, an ancient rambling two storey grey house with tiny windows and a crazy chimney stack looking in the dark like something straight from Dickens. I like old things. And this building was genuinely old – not purpose built old. I didn't know what it was. Betty thought it might be a pub. But there was nothing to suggest it was. No brazen advertising signs, no lager louts. No tacky coloured bulbs strung along the weather-beaten eaves, no plastic chairs and tables obstructing the footpath outside. Nothing. Maybe it was somebody's home. I couldn't resist a sideways glance at one of the slightly larger windows as we deliberately walked very slowly past. I just about managed to catch a glimpse of a dull electric light bulb dangling from a piece of flex close to the window. Plucking up courage, for it is not exactly the done thing to go peering through folk's windows, I did just that. I pressed my nose against the half curtained window and peered inside. In the dim light I could make out a couple of small round iron tables and a few odd chairs. A little lady of indeterminable age in a long dress and woollen cardigan sat in one of the chairs before an old iron stove warming her hands. Another figure, male, sat in the chimney corner. He seemed to be sipping at a glass of beverage.

I shook my head. "I'm not sure," I murmured to Betty. "Maybe it is a pub. But I don't really know. Should we take a peek through the door?"

I don't drink. Not even socially. A glass of wine at Christmas is fine to join in the spirit of the season. But wild horses wouldn't drag me into a pub. Now here I am, in a tiny town in the middle of nowhere, volunteering to push open a door which leads to where I had no idea, but might well be a pub.

I'm glad, very glad I lifted the latch and pushed open the ancient black door on that evening. I've pushed it open many times since then, always to be greeted by old and dear friends who have become very precious to us through the years. But now it was with some apprehension and soaking wet we stumbled down the small step into a tiny dark hall which seemed to lead nowhere. Suddenly, on our left hand side, another door opened in the dark panelling. The little lady I'd seen in front of the fire greeted us. "Good evening," she smiled in a beautiful and impeccable accent. "Do come in. Take off your wet coats. Hang them behind the door. They'll soon be dry."

Have you ever entered a room full of strangers, and immediately felt completely at home and at one with the company? Well, that's how Betty and I – even I who hated pubs – felt on that evening as we were welcomed in. The warmth of the welcome and the humour and the conversation we experienced that night was something you'd never find in an ordinary pub. The Three Tuns is the second oldest building in Hay, dating back to the fifteenth century. Only Hay castle is older. But The Three Tuns wasn't only a pub. It was a home, the dwelling-place of the little lady whom we soon discovered was Lucy Powell, owner of the premises. The Three Tuns had been in Lucy's family for generations. It seemed to me that apart from having an electric light bulb installed the pub had remained pretty much as Lucy's ancestors would have known it.

Lucy Powell is a living icon in Hay. She is known, loved, and respected by everyone – the locals, and friends from all over the world who have discovered her and taken her to their heart. Sometimes of an evening when the cold wind howls down from the Black Mountain, Lucy will drop her head and take a little doze in her seat by the fire. There is no other staff in The Three Tuns. Even the most thirsty customer will sit quietly with his empty glass in his hand, respectfully waiting until Lucy stirs, assures everyone she was not asleep, and offers to replenish the glass. In Lucy's you are not only a customer. You are a guest and a friend, and you conduct yourself accordingly. It is a privilege to be in Lucy's pub, and in her company. Lucy often receives letters from far away places, simply bearing the address "Lucy, The Three Tuns, Hay-on-Wye." They always arrive safely. Her unique little pub is frequently used by television and film crews in their productions of period dramas and documentaries. Why bother to build sets when the real thing, externally and internally, is sitting right there in Hay's Broad Street, in a perfectly natural environment.

Lucy often tells the tale of the time The Great Train Robbers, anxious, desperate, and on the run, came to hide out in Hay, miles from anywhere. The gang, fresh from the million pound heist of the Royal Mail train near Aylesbury, couldn't have chosen a worse hide-out. The good citizens of Hay could spot a stranger three valleys away. Lucy recognized the crooks immediately as they enjoyed a pint of her finest cider at The Three Tuns bar. But by the time Lucy hunted around for a telephone and a policeman – both rare commodities in Hay – the gang had gone. "Maybe just as well," laughs Lucy as she recounts the tale for the thousandth time. "They'd probably have come back to get me if they'd found out I'd shopped them!" Perhaps gang leader Ronnie Biggs, now back in Britain after years of enforced exile, might pay Lucy another visit. With no hard feelings. Just for old-times sake.

Our first night in The Three Tuns was also the night we met Haydn Pugh. Haydn owned the Photographic Bookshop up at the top of the town next door to the castle. If you've ever seen a photograph of Dylan Thomas you'll have a reasonable idea of Haydn's appearance. And what a sense of humour he has. The beautiful River Wye with its noble white swans and storks and herons flows elegantly at the foot of Hay and is forded by the old bridge which led up to our camp-site. "Lovely it is to meet you," smiled Haydn as he stretched out a strong and noble hand and welcomed us into the company of The Three Tuns. "I think I saw you earlier. On the Bridge over the River Wye!" Subtle, sparkling humour. We became instant friends. Now when we visit Hay, which is at least once a year, Haydn always prepares for us a very special dinner – four courses, superbly cooked by Haydn himself in his lovely little home just up the street from The Three Tuns.

Sid Wilding and his wife Lil are regulars at Lucy's. Sid and Lil are two more of the good friends we look forward to meeting up with every year. We usually take them a couple of pots of Betty's home-made blackberry jam. They reciprocate by pressing upon us a bottle of Sid's raspberry wine. It's his own brew, and usually well matured. Sid is book-buyer for Richard Booth's bookshop, though bookshop is hardly the right word. It's another building straight from Dickens, huge, rambling, umpteen floors and attics and cellars, housing maybe half a million second-hand books on any subject you care to name and ranging in price from a few pence to thousands of pounds per volume. Richard Booth, who lives in part of the castle and has turned the rest of it into another huge bookshop, was the man who single-handed changed Hay from an unknown backwater to the Town of Books, the term by which it is known world-wide today. Booth is an eccentric character and styles himself as the King of Hay. He's got the ermine robe and the crown to back up his claims and regularly makes a tilt at achieving independence for the tiny town. But if there is a rare book I need to find, Sid Wilding, King Richard's book-buyer, is the man to locate it. Like most of the regulars in Lucy's Sid enjoys a pint of "half and a half" – half beer and half cider, while his wife Lil draws on a cigarette and sips slowly at a glass of orange juice.

We stumbled out from The Three Tuns on that first evening long after closing time, when Lucy had closed the doors and insisted on making us tea and biscuits. "Have another," she encouraged us as we sipped at our tea. "They're very nice biscuits." They were. And we were to learn later it was a very rare and distinct honour for Lucy to invite anyone to tea in her premises after closing time. It was late, very late for Hay, when we eventually bade a fond good night to our new-found friend and set out over the bridge on the River Wye to tackle, just a little unsteadily, the hill which led to our campsite.

If Hay is lovely and fairytale-like by day it is even more beautiful and mystical by night. The rain had stopped now and the black velvet sky flooded with stars, larger and more numerous than any stars I had ever seen before. I thought I could reach out and touch the glittering torches and I was reminded of the scripture "the heavens declare the glory of God, the earth showth forth his handiwork." Not a sound, save the ghostly hoot of a tawny owl and the squeaking of bats flying across the pale moon. Half way up the hill I turned and looked back. I drank in the enchanting beauty of little Hay sleeping peacefully in the valley below, wrapped up in stillness and silence. The rambling old castle at the back of the town bathed in the gentle moonlight and the clock tower just down the street from it began to softly chime the midnight hour. Every time I visit Hay I always stop on the hill in the late evening. I always look back, savouring the beauty and peace so often searched for and so rarely found. I absorb the starry moonlit sky, the quiet town, its happy and contented citizens, far, far away from the mad and crazy rush of so-called civilization. Hay and its beautiful people are self-contained. They dwell in tranquillity. Even the world which beats a path to its door during the internationally famous Hay Literary Week cannot disturb it.

But there is a skeleton in gentle Hay's cupboard. Murder! Vile murder! On a bleak winter night on the 22nd of February 1921 – yesterday to most of Hay's venerable citizens – Mrs Katherine Armstrong, wife of Major Herbert Armstrong, died in mysterious circumstances in their elegant home on the outskirts of the sleepy town. On the final day of that year the Major was arrested on suspicion of murdering his wife by arsenic poisoning. Two days later Mrs Armstrong's body was exhumed and found to contain twice enough arsenic to kill an able-bodied man. The argument raged in the town and in the court as to whether Mrs Armstrong, not a well woman, had addicted herself to the poison, or whether the canny Major had administered it to her slowly over a period of time. The town was split on the right way of it then. It is still divided today. But Major Herbert Armstrong was found guilty of the dastardly crime of murder. He was hanged in Gloucester jail on the 31st of May 1922. Lucy's famous pub was used when yet another film of the mystery was produced a few years ago.

Richard Booth, self-styled King of Hay, has indeed made the town famous as the town of books. Some of the book shops are tiny. Some, like Booths, are massive. The Cinema Bookshop is just that, the old Castle Cinema converted into a bookshop. Several miles of shelving house almost half a million books. There are shops devoted to second-hand Penguin books. There's a Children's Bookshop. Another specialises in Dickens, others on the American Indian, boxing, antiquarian, theology or whatever your taste may be. One shop sells only jigsaw-puzzles – hundreds of them – and Teddybears. There's a little picnic area where you can enjoy a packed lunch while the red squirrels scramble about at your feet. The sun-dappled trees above your head whisper secrets and the silver River Wye flows majestically and musically at your feet. Well did Wordsworth pen the words when he wrote: "O sylvan Wye! Thou wanderer thro' the woods, How often has my spirit turned to thee!

One winter night, not long after Christmas, we received a telephone call from Hay-on-Wye. It was Haydn. Lucy had suffered a bad fall in the night when she was all alone in The Three Tuns. It was the next day before her absence on the streets of Hay and the closed doors of her pub prompted a hue and cry to discover what had happened to Hay's favourite citizen. When Haydn and a few friends found Lucy she was immediately despatched to hospital where she was now quite ill. The Three Tuns was closed. Indefinitely. Haydn didn't overly commit himself but I could tell by the tone of his voice he was concerned. It seemed it might be the end of the road, if not for Lucy, then probably for The Three Tuns.

But Lucy Powell is nothing if not a fighter. This tiny lady with the indomitable spirit and never say die attitude fought back to an amazing recovery in a very short time. "Hugh," enthused Haydn, as he kept us informed by almost daily telephone calls, "you wouldn't believe it! Lucy's blooming like a rose! She's better than I've ever seen her – and she's talking about opening again at Easter!"

Lucy didn't just talk about opening. She did it. But unknown to Lucy, Haydn and a multitude of other locals had got wind it was almost her birthday and secretly lined up a surprise party for Lucy in her own pub. Everybody in Hay and for miles around were in on the big secret. Everybody except Lucy, who probably wouldn't have sanctioned such a fuss being made over her. But friends would be travelling from everywhere to be present. Any chance we could make it?

Any chance! Betty and I were on the first boat out from Larne, then belting down the motorway several days in advance of the big shindig. We were about to become part of the Hay conspiracy.

I've had some terrific nights in The Three Tuns with Lucy and Haydn and Sid and Lil and the rest of the gang. But that birthday hooley for Hay's favourite lady was the best of the best. Not knowing the scale of the conspiracy being hatched around her Lucy had agreed to let Haydn string her birthday cards and a few streamers around the bar. On the morning of the grand celebration birthday I had the honour of helping Haydn decorate The Three Tuns. Minimal it wasn't. We slung the twisted coloured streamers diagonally from the four corners of the ceiling and the dozens of birthday cards on three lines of cord right across the front of the bar. A dozen balloons suspended above the smooth and well worn settle seats added to the colour and even Lucy, who doesn't waste words, declared it to be "very nice."

They came from everywhere – on foot, by car, on bicycles, by boat and by train – to honour Lucy. The bemused expression on Lucy's face blended with amazement and not a little emotion as the tiny pub filled to overflowing with well-wishers, bouquets of flowers, *three* birthday cakes, more cards, a bag of best Irish turf to keep the fire blazing merrily, and loads of home-made eatables to stave off the hunger pangs on what promised to be a long but very enjoyable night. The party was, as everyone agreed, more than just a birthday party. It was a long overdue tribute to Lucy, to express in a very small way the high esteem in which this wonderful lady is held by so many people.

It finally got to the point where the little hostelry simply could not contain all the well-wishers trying to gain admittance. Lucy was obliged to open up her small back parlour – her private quarters – where I eased the strain by taking twenty or thirty of the happy band in with me and regaling them with a bit of storytelling about Lucy, and The Three Tuns, and Hay, and what they all meant to me. It was a great honour to tell the stories in Lucy's parlour. Apparently it was the first time any of the locals had seen the other side of the parlour door.

Even Richard Booth, book-baron and King of Hay, came to pay court to Lucy. Then he surprised me by coming up and introducing himself to me. Nice man, that King! Mr Alan Swainston Cooper, he of The Temperance Seven band fame also arrived to raise a glass to Lucy and to play Happy Birthday for her on his clarinet. I was able to share some time in Lucy's parlour with this most interesting and convivial gentleman, probing into the early days of The Temperance Seven, how the band got started, and how such an unusual line-up of musicians who played 1920's music in 1920's style on 1920's instruments were able to hold their own with the Beatles and the Rolling Stones in the swinging sixties. The talented band even had several hits, including the number one chart topper "You're Driving Me Crazy." Nowadays Mr Cooper, though still musically active, looks, in his country tweeds and plus-fours and sucking on his favourite briar, more a country squire than a jazz musician. But to add to all her other claims to fame, Miss Lucy Powell can point to the fact she has had "Happy Birthday" played to her by a gentleman who was once upon a time number one in the pop charts.

As Haydn Pugh and everyone else acknowledges, Lucy's charm has won her friends from all over the world. I am privileged to be one of them. On behalf of all her admirers in The Three Tuns that birthday night I was honoured to be chosen to make a little speech signifying something of what Lucy meant to each one of us, and to present her with an "Oscar" for being Hay's most respected and most loved citizen.

Come to Hay. Even if you are not a book-lover. Even if you are a tee-totaller! You will be enchanted by its genuine old-world simplicity, the warmth of its people, the beauty of the town itself, the romantic valley it lies in, and the grandeur of the Black Mountain above. You will fall in love with Hay as it weaves its magic spell over you, as it has done to me. It will become your own Brigadoon, where, for just a little while, you will dwell in a magical place time has forgotten and where old values and old pleasures still obtain.

I can't wait any longer. I'm off. To Hay. But this time I'm going to hang a little note on my door.

Come in. Make yourself at home.
I may be gone for a long time. A very long time.
I've gone. Gone to Hay. The Town that time forgot.
Hay, The Town of Books.

To Russia with Love

In the summer of 1997 I achieved a lifetime ambition. I visited Russia. Russia – land of the Czars, Cossacks, Tolstoy and Tchaikovsky, the Steppes, and of course, the mighty Volga River, known and loved by the Russian people as Mother Volga.

For two glorious weeks my wife Betty and I cruised from St. Petersburg on the edge of the Baltic to Moscow, via the River Neva, across Lake Ladoga, which is so vast you cannot see the opposite shore, and down the Volga itself. Our transport was the beautifully appointed cruise ship Andropov. Not being a gentleman of leisure, nor of independent means, I do not normally go on cruises. But this cruise I had chosen very deliberately and with a good deal of care. It would suit my purposes admirably. I wanted to see Russia. But I didn't want a tour directed by the state Intourist machine telling me what I should see and where and when to see it. I wanted to meet real Russians in every day situations and experience something of their life as they lived it. I'd studied all the literature sent out by the cruise company.

By sailing along the Russian rivers and waterways, through the country heartland, I knew there was a good chance I'd get close to the spirit of Russia and its people. The magnificent cultural and architectural glories of Moscow and St. Petersburg would be worthwhile bonuses.

That's the way it turned out. We sailed the tranquil waterways past rolling landscapes of small farms, silver birch woods, old villages which time seemed to have forgotten, churches and cathedrals with their amazing onion-domed cupolas, and on into the magical Golden Ring cities of Holy Russia with their kremlins and monasteries. We visited the Winter Palace of Peter the Great, experienced the Kirov ballet, enjoyed the spectacular Moscow State Circus and the St. Petersburg Symphony Orchestra. And more. But most importantly, we had the great privilege and honour of being entertained by Russian peasants in their little ramshackle wooden homes deep in the depths of the Russian countryside. I use the word peasant in its proper form and with the greatest respect. As a child growing up in the countryside of Ballyhay, near Donaghadee, I experienced life similar to what I found around me on the Russian smallholdings. Simplicity, and make-do were the keynotes.

There is no doubt in my mind my country childhood in Ballyhay formed the basis of my fascination with Russia – a vast and mysterious land covering one sixth of the earth's total land-mass, several time-zones and so far removed geographically, but perhaps not culturally from my own cottage home in County Down. As I studied my reading book in Ballyvester school I formed the opinion that little Ivan and his family had much in common with mine. They also struggled to eke out a living on a few acres of ground with two or three bits of livestock. The winter nights in Russia were long and cold and dark, just as they were in Ballyhay. But for the Russian peasant it was so much more difficult, being snowed and frozen in for six months of the year. So it was from the written word I gained my first awareness of the Russian people. My second came by the spoken word.

One dark winter night as the wind howled and screeched and the snow piled up outside our lonely home I sat with my grandparents and my sister Ann by the fireside. We were gathered in a sort of semi-circle listening to a play on the wireless. The battery was almost exhausted and the reception was poor. I remember practically nothing of the play except that it was about some travellers crossing a great unexplored land and becoming lost. Finally they encountered some of the native people of that great country and enquired the name of the land they had come to. The one word reply – threatening, filled with mystery – thrilled me, yet filled my young heart with foreboding and fear. "Russo!" was the reply, in a deep growling voice and in an accent I could barely understand. I couldn't wait to get to school the next day to find out where Russo was on the map of the world. I discovered the modern day name was Russia. I was staggered when I looked at the map hanging on the wall. Russia seemed to cover half the world's surface. As I studied the tiny United Kingdom I was afraid it would be curtains for us if Russia ever engaged us in mortal combat.

In later years I devoured the works of Tolstoy, Chekov, and Dostoevsky. Tolstoy was my favourite. Not only was he a majestic writer whose magnificent works laid bare to me the vast Russian landscape and every aspect of its society – he revealed the very soul of Russia as well. I was pleased that, although on a vastly greater scale than us, Tolstoy was also a land-owner. I empathized with this tall bearded author who spent so much of his time working in the hayfields with his serfs, much as I had worked in the fields with old men with moustaches and beards not unlike Tolstoy's. I learned to appreciate something of the hardness of life for the people of this vast continent and of their indomitable will to be free despite repeated invasions through the centuries, culminating in recent history in their refusal to bow the knee to Napoleon and Hitler.

I had a passion for Russia, and for the Russian people I had never met. But I wanted to meet them on their own farms, in their *dachas*, speak with them in their own language and sip *chi* (tea) with them at their own table. Now I was about to do it. For weeks prior to our departure I had slaved over Russian textbooks and recordings of the Russian language, trying to learn a little of it so I would be able to communicate with the people I met.

The first part of our journey by plane from Heathrow to St. Petersburg took about four and a half hours. Russia is vast. Though it has mountains, and high ones at that, most of the country is flat. And that's what I viewed from my window seat. A flat never-ending land intersected with many canals and broad straight roads without bends scarring the countryside. As our jet descended low over old St. Petersburg, I wondered what my first sight of life in Russia would be. It was a little bird, something akin to a sparrow, alighting in a tree as we glided in for touch-down. Then I saw a female airport worker on the tarmac in the distance. I would see many female workers in Russia occupied in manual jobs - scything grass, working on building sites and brushing the streets with old type brooms made from twigs.

I cannot speak too highly, in every respect, of Russia and its people, whatever their position in society. But St. Petersburg air-port, or at least the arrivals section, was a law onto itself, primitive and chaotic. The arrivals area was a huge marble building with practically nothing inside. No bookstalls. No cafes. No information desks. Nothing save three tall wooden sentry-like boxes to which we now – to use the term loosely – queued to have our passports checked. As I handed my documents over to the pretty but unsmiling uniformed Russian lady at the box I decided I would, just to be sociable, try out my Russian language skills. "*Dobrii dyen*," I enunciated, laying the stresses where I thought they would be most effective and smiling bravely as I waited for the spark of interest and cheery greeting for a foreigner who had taken the trouble to brush up on the local lingo. Nothing. Only a cold and suspicious stare, and a firmer grip on my passport, which immediately caused me to believe I had already committed a criminal act of espionage on Russian soil and would be incarcerated forthwith pending despatch to outer Siberia.

I needn't have worried. Although there is much humour in the Russian psyche – Russian people are the kindest and friendliest I have ever met – it seems there is a time and a place for everything. You do not get familiar or attempt to crack a joke with any Russian in uniform. Not even the *babushka*, the old headscarfed women who act as suspicious caretakers and guardians in any place of interest you care to visit in Russia. It seems once they don a uniform – and the *babushka* doesn't even need that – and achieve authority of any degree they immediately cast off their own personal identity and become a total representation of whatever office or authority has been invested in them. Any attempt to make conversation which is not directly related to the terms of the authority held is an immediate cause of the deepest suspicion, as is any act which deviates from the supposed norm.

I removed the smile from my face and cowed before the checker of passports, my mouth tightly closed as she slowly and with great deliberation studied all my papers, occasionally taking a closer look at me with cold eyes to determine I was indeed who I represented myself to be. Finally, with a withering look, and a quick nod of the head, she motioned me through. Not as confident as before I hesitated, fearing a step across the yellow line on the floor might be construed as an act of open aggression and invasion of the Motherland. "*Bistrah*!" exclaimed my uniformed Russian beauty. "Quickly!" I crossed the yellow line. Quickly. Not wishing to be rude or seen to hold a grudge, I mumbled a quiet "thank you." In English. If there was a response, I didn't hear it.

We reclaimed our luggage and joined the melee of passengers trying to find the customs forms which needed to be filled out and read by more officialdom. Finally, on a glorious summer afternoon, we struggled free from the terminal and bureaucracy which is everywhere in Russia and boarded the smoky wreck of a bus which rumbled us through the historic streets of St. Petersburg to the Andropov berthed on the River Neva.

St. Petersburg, formerly Leningrad, and previous to that St. Petersburg again, seems to change its name every few years in relation to whatever political power is in the ascendancy at the time. It is a beautiful city, built by Peter the Great in the mainly classical style, to emulate the great cities of Europe. Formerly the capital of all Russia it is still artistically, aristocratically and architectually superior to Moscow. Like all Russian cities the streets are long and straight and broad for there is no want of space anywhere. There is much grandeur. This is the city of the Winter Palace of the Czars, The Hermitage and the glorious St. Isaac's Cathedral. It is home to art galleries and museums housing thousands of the world's finest treasures. There is also poverty. Many of the city's old buildings and streets have run down and gone to seed for the want of funds in an economy which is at best volatile. But the child of Russia will speak of nothing but good of his homeland. As our bus groaned through some of St. Petersburg's more ordinary streets our guide – there is always a guide – lifted her microphone and spoke in her quaint but charming English.

"Please, dear friends. Please be kind enough to look through your left hand window. You will see one of our citizens taking his dog for a walk along one of our lovely avenues. No doubt he is on his way to one of our beautiful parks, so many of which we have in our fine city." Such pride. Not in an arrogant sense, but in appreciation of the fact her fellow-citizen had the right as well as the facilities to take his dog for a walk in a park if he felt so inclined. Somehow I couldn't envisage a Belfast tour guide enthusing about a man and his dog on their way to Ormeau Park. But that set the tone for the entire visit – the warm and grateful heart the Russian has for any good that may be done to him or for him.

The Andropov was a beautifully equipped vessel with three decks, superb and friendly staff (no official uniforms!) and nestling in the sun-lit waters of the quiet Neva. As we stepped down from our coach at the quayside we were serenaded by a little Russian folk group. Before boarding the ship which would be our transport and home for the next fortnight, we were offered the traditional hospitality of bread and salt by a pretty Russian girl in national costume.

After we'd settled into our spacious cabin and made ourselves presentable, we enjoyed a superb Russian dinner in the ship's restaurant. Russians are big on vegetables, any vegetables, lightly cooked – or better still raw – cheese, soups, eggs and fish – not quite so strong on meat, which for whatever reason rarely appeared on our plate. But Russian ice-cream has to be tasted to be believed. Russians adore it. So did we.

We spent two days in St. Petersburg, which has a population of about four million. The main street, Nevsky Prospect, which features in so much Russian literature, is two and a half straight miles long, and about six traffic lanes wide. Contrary to popular belief there is an abundance of shops and plenty of things to buy, food or otherwise, provided you have the money. Tourists always have the money. In the Russian economy we felt we were millionaires as we saw the things we could buy so cheaply with our dollars. We could travel the underground all day long for about two pence and afford the best of Russian produce and artwork. The trouble with Russian shops is that from the outside you just don't know they are shops. Often they look just like an ordinary house and even if you do identify one it's difficult to establish what it might sell. The front windows are generally very small and display little or nothing of what may be for sale inside. Entrance is gained by the normally closed small door which gives no clue what lies behind. A few of the bigger shops, like Littlewoods, are the exception and are a little more easily identified. In some of the larger stores we were immediately offered the hospitality of a large vodka which we were expected to down forthwith and come back for more. At no charge. Maybe it was typical Russian friendliness. Maybe it also aided in the loosening of the purse strings.

It is impossible to describe the splendour of the cathedrals and palaces of St. Petersburg – the Winter Palace, the Hermitage, the Peterhoff Palace, nor the artistic masterpieces they contain. I have seen the great palaces of London and Paris and Versailles. I could only stand in awe at the glory that is St. Petersburg.

But there is poverty here, just as there is in any country or city in which you care to set your foot. Old women in rough overcoats and the ubiquitous headscarves hang about the places haunted by tourists – the cathedrals, palaces and art galleries. Sometimes thin and gaunt, sometimes fat and shapeless, and always seemingly too ancient of days to be on the streets at all, their long overcoats have seen better days and their once bright and vibrantly coloured headscarves have dulled and faded like the eyes of their owners. They beg, not verbally, for such an open display of poverty would be beneath the dignity of any Russian no matter how hungry, but in complete silence, fixing one with imploring and longing eyes which speak more than a thousand words. Sometimes the *babushka* – the term is used for Russian grandmothers, female caretakers and just plain old women – clutch tiny bunches of wild flowers they have garnered from the fields on the edge of the city. The flowers are little more than weeds. But at least the *babushka* has something to offer in exchange for a few *kopeks.* And dignity is maintained.

Betty and I were aware we would encounter need on our travels. We came prepared and brought three suitcases, One contained Betty's clothes. One held mine. The contents of the third we would pass on to those we reckoned needed it most. Soap, talcum, chocolate, toothpaste, pens, socks, gloves, colouring books and coloured pencils and sweets for the children. Some clothing. Nothing to us. Riches for some.

It was on our first visit to the Hermitage, which contains a breathtaking display of Russian and European art and priceless artifacts from all over the world, I had my first taste of the poverty which always seems to exist side by side with riches and untold wealth. As I stepped down from the bus just short of the

Hermitage I was aware of a small thin lady standing a little to my side. She spoke no word as our eyes met. She didn't need to. Though unfamiliar with the country and its people, I saw her need. I was also unfamiliar with the *kopeks* and *roubles* which bulged my wallet. I moved closer to the old lady and gently pushed a fair handful of Russian coins into her hand. "*Padarak.* Gift," I said. Tears streamed from the old lady's eyes as her hand closed on the coins. She grasped both my hands and kissed them and thanked me over and over again, repeatedly making the sign of the cross. I hadn't expected such a response. I nodded my head and smiled, signifying I understood her thanks. I put my arms around her and we hugged each other. Words were not required to tell what was in each of our hearts. Then I turned away as the old lady continued to wave her thanks and make the sign of the cross. I didn't feel too good about the whole episode when later that evening I did a rough calculation of the money I'd given her. It was pathetic. About two pence. Two miserable pennies. I made another mistake, fortunately in the opposite manner, about a week later. Meaning to give another old lady who was leaning heavily on a stick the equivalent of one pound, I gave her, without realizing it, just over five pounds worth of *roubles.* I couldn't stem the tears from my own eyes as this dear lady sobbed loudly, hugged and kissed me and thanked me and would not let me take my leave from her. It was only later that evening when I again did a calculation I realised I'd probably given the old lady more *roubles* than she'd ever seen in one place at one time in all her long life. The five pounds wouldn't alter my life. It might very well have changed hers. We'd given her a few other little gifts and I wished we had arranged for a container load of stuff to give away instead of the contents of a measly suitcase. Of course even the contents of a container wouldn't have registered in the great need of the Russian elderly who live on a miserly pension, and that often not paid for months at an end.

After two days exploring the glories of St. Petersburg our floating home set sail on a splendid summer evening along the Neva, toward Lake Ladoga and eventually the Volga and Moscow, and all points in between. There was sadness in my heart as I leaned over the rail and waved goodbye to a couple of dozen citizens who blew kisses to us and returned our waves. We had enjoyed the friendship of the St. Petersburg people. They were travellers too, on the sea of life. Our paths had crossed for a brief period. As we called "dahsveedahneeah" to our friends on the quayside we knew it was unlikely they would cross again.

After a delightful Russian dinner I returned to the deck near midnight as the Andropov eased along the broad and peaceful river. I experienced the beauty of the Russian "White Night" so named because at midnight the sun had still not retired behind the horizon. At half past one in the morning I was still writing notes in my cabin without the need of artificial light.

The Andropov usually sailed by night. Every morning we awoke to another new town or city or village and more new experiences. So much to see, to do, to learn, usually in the company of our teenage female guides - students, who beyond a shadow of doubt loved their homeland and delighted in explaining in excellent English its many charms to those who had come to visit it. I had never before encountered a people who loved the land of their birth as the Russians loved theirs. And when imparting a new piece of information to us our guides always addressed us as "Dear friends". There was plenty to do on board the Andropov and every evening a superb little folk band played into the wee small hours. I got to know the musicians quite well – their cabin was next to ours – and there was no problem if I asked them to play a particular tune. Another student taught basic Russian including the important word "*deshevla*" – "what is the least amount of money you will take for this item?" – which came in very handy at the street markets. Not that we used the word very often. So much of the superb Russian handicrafts and original works of art were available at give away prices – if you were a tourist. Not necessarily a rich tourist. Just an ordinary tourist like us.

The street markets in the towns and villages were another learning curve for me. More *babushki*, sitting on stools or perhaps even the ground, with something akin to an empty orange box in front of them. The orange box was their stall on which to display the produce. The produce usually consisted of a single fish or a bunch of spring onions or a beetroot. Not all three. Only one item, and that was the sum total of the stock each *babushka* had to sell.

One of the highlights and warmest memory of my first journey through Russia was the "green stop" we made at Irma, smack in the middle of the Russian countryside before we joined the mighty Volga. The massive Andropov simply pulled into the river bank and we were free to strike out into the warm green fields and dusty brown dirt-track roads to discover what we could. Betty and I climbed a small green hill gleaming with tiny yellow flowers much like buttercups. Over the hill lay a field of golden corn, a small hayfield, a few small wooden homes, and a few goats and hens and the occasional cow rambling about at their leisure. But the land was open, as far as the eye could see, with no attempt to fence off or contain what property or stock might belong to one particular person. In Russia there is plenty of room for all.

We wandered aimlessly through the fields enjoying the rural tranquillity of the warm summer day. Close to one of the wooden houses a man, maybe in his sixties, began to wave to us and encourage us to come over and join him at his home. This was exactly what I wanted. We ambled over and bade the man "*dobri-utra*" – good-morning. This seemed to please him and he returned our greeting with a broad smile as he doffed his cap and ushered us toward the front door. We pushed our way through two or three hens scraping in the red dust around the door and respectfully entered a narrow hallway. The man, still smiling, and even laughing, followed us in, with a couple of the hens in close attendance. The hallway obviously doubled up as a store. It was filled with every sort of useful household utensil imaginable

– white enamel buckets, a couple of spades, a crock of milk, a hall-stand which held two or three sheaves of corn and a scythe casually tossed against the wall at exactly the right level to lop your foot off at the ankle if you were at all careless. I could smell the warm milk in the crock and reckoned it was well on its way to turning. Not that that would spoil the Russian appetite. We passed into a sparsely but cleanly furnished bright little room. A middle-aged woman dressed in the usual Russian country manner spread her arms wide open and welcomed us to her home. She fussed around, smiling all the while, obviously delighted to see us. The man, who didn't tell us his name, informed us the woman was his wife Vera. He also introduced the perhaps teenage boy who sprawled on an old sofa which had seen better days as Sergi, his grandson. Then he doffed his cap, bowed, and retreated up the hall and out the door. We never saw him again. We later realized the man had done his job. Now it was up to Vera.

We communicated with Vera in our limited Russian as she showed us around her little home. The most valuable thing in it, apart from the huge television, was probably the silver samovar which sat on the square wooden table by the window. But as Vera proudly showed us around it was obvious the most precious thing to her was the faded black and white portrait of her parents hanging on one of the wooden walls close to the icon in the corner. Vera went to great lengths to tell us every detail about her deceased parents. All Russians hold their ancestors in the highest respect and honour. Vera waved an arm and bade us be seated at the table. We sat down on the hard wooden chairs and gazed through the window at the rolling hay fields and corn fields and the other tourists wandering about. From seemingly nowhere Vera suddenly produced a large pile of *bleeni* (pancakes), a small dish of jam, a sugar bowl, a jug of cream and four glacier sweets. I sensed this was a grand table for Vera to set. She beamed with obvious pride and pleasure as she set down the cups and saucers. In turn, it was a moving experience for us to be invited into the home of complete strangers and to enjoy such hospitality. Just before we departed from the little home we left a few dollars on the table to show our appreciation. We learned later that this was the whole object of the exercise – the hope that the guests invited in might be gracious enough to leave a small "*padarak*" which would be humbly accepted with much appreciation and go some way to helping the family through another of the harsh Russian winters. It was a sort of unspoken trade-off which was pleasing to both parties.

We had a similar experience an hour later as we continued our rambles through the countryside. As we passed by another old wooden house with a green picket fence and a little garden of potatoes and tall sunflowers, a woman, maybe in her thirties, staking the sunflowers, greeted us as we passed by. Always eager to engage the Russian, I opened a little conversation.

"Is this your home?" I queried. "Do you live here?"

"*Nyet*," replied the woman. "This is my mother's house. Would you like to meet her?"

Of course we would. Again the house was modestly furnished, the wooden walls painted a dull matt yellow and a couple of pictures hanging on them to take away the plainness. An icon took pride of place on a corner shelf. A table sat below the window, just as in Vera's, and an elderly slim and smiling lady sat at it. Anastasia was maybe eighty years old with long grey hair most of which was concealed by the typically bright Russian headscarf. A sort of rough housecoat covered her thin body. She spoke something in Russian and grinned and pointed to the chairs around the table. Having a pretty good idea of what was about to happen we sat down. As in Vera's, the *bleeni* and *chi* and good things to eat appeared from nowhere, but this time accompanied by a tall and pretty lethal looking bottle of vodka and several glasses. I thought of the potatoes growing outside the front door. Many Russians make their own vodka. From potatoes. Anastasia poured the vodka herself and she wasn't mean with it. I don't drink. But I knew this was an offering of welcome to the home and of friendship. I would have to "pass myself", as we say in Northern Ireland, make an attempt to accept the hospitality. I sipped slowly at the vodka. Anastasia frowned as she watched me.

"*Nyet*! *Nyet*!" she scolded and motioned me to observe as she downed her brimming glass in one gulp and invited me to do the same. The vodka hadn't seemed to have done Anastasia much harm. I flung my head back and downed the contents of my glass. I choked and spluttered and gasped for breath as the fiery flames burned into my stomach and into my brain as Anastasia rolled about in her chair, bursting with raucous laughter and hammering her fist on the table. Finally, seeing I was far from making any sort of recovery, she dug a spoonful of sugar from the sugar bowl and motioning me to open my mouth, rammed it down my throat. The Russian people have many excellent folk cures and antidotes. Ingesting large amounts of sugar to deflect the ravages of vodka is not one of the more successful.

We spent quite a bit of time in Anastasia's home. Before we took our leave she took special pride in showing us a portrait of her late brother Alexander and also pointed reverently to the icon on the wall, just in case we had missed it. I will always remember Anastasia. She was happy to receive the little "*padarak*" we left behind.

We met many people at Irma on that sunny day. A few citizens had travelled the dusty roads from one of the outlying towns to set up souvenir stalls in the middle of the fields, well aware the cruise ships would be making a stop. At we stopped at one of the stalls to examine the wares we got into conversation with the stall-holder. Angelique was a young good looking schoolteacher with long blonde hair held back across her forehead with a red headband. But she wasn't school-teaching at Irma. Doctors, the military, and school-teachers have the honour – or misfortune – to belong to the worst paid professions in Russia. To supplement her meagre earnings Angelique was obliged to travel from her town to Irma in the tourist season during the school holidays to make a few extra *roubles*. I bought from Angelique a beautiful hand-painted plate depicting a Russian church in the snow-covered birch woods with a black sky above. To make it more personal I asked Angelique if she would sign the plate. She did, on the back, with a felt tip marker. It takes pride of place on the wall in our living-room. We took a photograph of Angelique and then one of Angelique and Betty and I together. Angelique gave us her address and asked if we would send her a print. When we returned home we sent the photographs and a little letter. We received a written reply from Angelique. Four pages of beautiful Russian handwriting – a work of art in itself – but not one word of which I could understand. A friend of ours in Newtownards, Mrs Plunkett, who does much in the way of relief work for Russian people, kindly translated for us. That was the beginning of a regular correspondence and a warm friendship which was to open up for us further and even more fulfilling journeys to Russia and ties with the Russian people.

Further along the Volga, near the Moscow Canal but still well outside the city in the countryside, the Andropov made an unscheduled stop, literally right against the river bank. We weren't allowed to disembark. Anyway, there were no facilities to do so. It seemed someone was coming on board by tender to ensure the crew and passengers were medically safe to enter Moscow. It would be nothing more than another piece of Russian formality without any teeth. No one was examined. The passengers, anxious to find out what had caused the sudden stop lined the rails and gazed across the fields of flowers to a little green hill perhaps a quarter of a mile away. Suddenly half a dozen *babushki*, not slim, cleared the hill from the other side and came sprinting toward the ship as hard as they could. The women seemed desperate to reach us. They were perhaps middle-aged, headscarf-tails flying in the breeze as they laughed and shouted words which I could not understand. I didn't know why they wanted to reach us, but there was no doubt they did, and before the ship moved off. The women clambered right down to the river bank, waving and shouting and grinning at us and almost falling into the water as they reached up to the rail and offered us tiny bunches of red and yellow and purple wild flowers and little paper bags bursting with red berries. Suddenly I realized what was happening. The women had been out in the fields picking flowers and berries to sell in the town. Suddenly, and without prior knowledge, this huge cruise ship had pulled in practically beside them. The market had come to them, a ship-full of affluent tourists. What a bonus!

I dashed down the couple of decks to our cabin and our third suitcase. I grabbed as much stuff as I could carry and hurried back up to the rail. I showered the jovial ladies with soap and combs and fruit and chocolates and small items of clothing. The women scrambled around, feverishly grabbing as the manna dropped from heaven while my fellow-travellers stared at them and at me in amazement. I knew my well-heeled shipmates were not aware of the need and that perhaps I was displaying something of my own social background by attempting to tend to it. That didn't bother me. But I was delighted when they too began to toss bits and pieces over the rails. The women on the river bank reached up, trying to press bags of berries and flowers into my hands. "*Nyet! Nyet!*," I shouted in my best Northern Ireland Russian. "I don't need! You keep. Sell in town!" But these poor women pleaded with tears in their eyes for me to accept their gifts in exchange for the gifts I had given to them, and continued until I relented. How they laughed and waved and blew kisses and tried to give more as the Andropov began to pull away. I waved and called out "dahsveedahneeah" until we lost sight of each other. I marvelled again at the warmth of heart and kindness and the spirit of these dear people. I would never see them again. But I would never forget them.

The excitement over, we retired to our cabin and I took a shower to freshen myself up. "Did you see the bag of berries the ladies gave you?" Betty asked me when I came out from the little bathroom.

"Of course I saw it," I replied. "Didn't I give it to you to put in the fridge?"

"But did you really look at it," insisted Betty. She opened the door of the fridge and pulled out the bag. "Here. Take a close look."

The "bag" was nothing more than a sheet of tabloid newspaper, folded over and hand sown around the edges with needle and white cotton to form a bag. Nothing is discarded in Russia. Everything has its use. For the good of your soul, before you die dear friend, visit Russia.

Moscow is a vast city over fifty miles wide. Staggeringly big, it's the home of the famous Red Square, the Kremlin, the Bolshoi Ballet, the Moscow State Circus and some of Russia's most amazing and colourful onion-domed cathedrals, the most spectacular of which is St. Basil's. Moscow is a vast and affluent city. The very best of everything is available here in one of the most expensive cities in the world. But Betty's taste in Moscow was easily and inexpensively satisfied. She enjoyed a Big Mac in McDonalds.

Red Square isn't really a square. Nor is it red. It's a rectangle and its well-worn cobblestones are dirty-brown, though they may well once have been red. They've certainly witnessed plenty of Russia's troubled history. But there is much disagreement as to why Red Square is so called. In centuries gone the place was simply a spacious area used for fairs and markets. It was also used for public executions, giving rise to the theory the spilling of blood on the ancient stones may have given the place its unusual name. But that's only one of the theories – as with all things Russian nothing is ever what it seems or purports to be. The Square is surrounded by the Kremlin – which is just another name for a fortifying wall and there are kremlins all over Russia. St. Basil's Cathedral and Lenin's Mausoleum lay close by. The mausoleum lies within the Kremlin walls deep down behind another solid red marble edifice. There is always a queue to see Lenin, or what remains of him. It stretches along the side of the Square and out into another street. It usually takes about half an hour to get to the head of the queue. If you happen to have a camera on you, or in your possession, you'll be turned away to queue all over again – without your camera. We were.

Upon entering the mausoleum you walk down broad brown marble steps, almost in darkness, maximum two or three persons at a time. It is forbidden to speak. At the bottom of the steps you turn right where you get a glimpse on your left hand side of Lenin, high forehead and almost yellow face, under glass, lying as though he just died, in a dark morning suit. You walk along the side of the glass entombed body, around the foot, past the single Red Army guard, along the other side, and out. From first catching sight of the body until leaving takes about twenty seconds. Stopping to stare is strictly forbidden.

During our two days in Moscow we crammed in as much as we possibly could, which of course means we didn't see a fraction of the place. We did manage to visit the house of Tolstoy and many of the fabulous palaces. And of course a visit to the Moscow Circus was a must.

The circus wasn't held in a tent. Home to the Moscow State Circus is a typically huge and what appeared to be a marble building on Tsvetnoy Boulevard. The inside is what you'd expect if you were attending a ballet – plush foyers, ante-rooms, bars and restaurants and a glorious auditorium with red cushioned seats and central heating. I observed again the impeccable Russian manners during our visit for a performance due to start at eight o'clock. At about two minutes after eight the performance hadn't begun. I was puzzled as a gentle ripple of applause travelled right around the auditorium from the audience for no particular reason. This happened two or three times. Then I realized what was happening. Back home, if a performance is delayed, the audience might well stamp their feet, slow hand-clap or maybe even whistle in derision. I believe the Russian audience were saying to the circus performers behind the scenes – "listen to our applause for you – see how much we appreciate what you are going to do for us even though we have not yet seen you do anything! Please come out and entertain us! Thank you!" And the circus performers did entertain. In spectacular fashion.

Moscow by night is a wondrous sight. And the Moscow Metro far surpassed all I had ever heard or read about it. Marble walls, leaded lights, crystal chandeliers and works of art grace every station. Each stop along the line is a small palace which just happens to have a train running through it. No advertisements. No graffiti. Just artistic beauty and grandeur. Everywhere. We travelled several stations on the underground. For most of the journey I was mildly amused to find myself sitting beside an old woman in a tightly buttoned overcoat and headscarf, and clutching a red plastic bucket filled with eggs. Typically Russian.

My most abiding memory of our Moscow visit was our return to Red Square – this time by night. It was about half an hour to midnight. The Kremlin and Red Square and St. Basil's are spectacular in the daytime. By night, floodlit, and with a crescent moon hanging in a starry sky, they are astonishingly and spectacularly beautiful, almost like a fairyland. The gold and red and green cupolas of St. Basil's gleamed magically as they were picked out by unseen floodlights. And the silence. We were only a few yards from the city's main thoroughfares. But all was quiet, silent, save for the muffled sound of gentle footsteps on the ancient cobbles. And now, most beautiful of all, the clock tower, gold and black and high above us in the Kremlin wall, pealing out the chimes of midnight. Midnight in Moscow! Midnight in Red Square, the very heart of Russian history. As I gazed at all things essentially Russian around me I could hardly believe I was standing here in this mysterious and historic place which was closed to the western world for so many years. I thought again of my childhood home in Ballyhay – a world away from here – and little Ivan in my storybooks, and Vera and Anastasia in their little wooden shacks, and their simplicity and kindness. It had been a long journey for me, in distance, and in years. But I was here in the heart of this beautiful land and its lovely people for whom life is a daily struggle which they face with such equanimity. My heart was at one with the nation and its people. And although I didn't know it then, the earlier chance meeting with the school-teacher Angelique would result in a return to Russia during which we would experience in a very real way what it is to live in that land as a normal citizen and without any of the trappings of tourism surrounding us. But more of that in a later chapter.

I'm often asked if I would recommend a visit to Russia. The answer is of course a resounding "yes". Especially if you have a feeling or passion for the country. Do not delay. The generosity and warmth of the Russian spirit will overwhelm you. There is beauty everywhere, and especially in the Russian soul. Hospitality exceeds even the famed Northern Ireland welcome. You will return to your own homeland, wherever that may be, humbled, wiser, and richer in spirit. Your heart will be flooded with warm and happy memories. And the saddest word you will speak in the Russian tongue, as you take your leave, is "Dahsveedahneeah!". Goodbye.

Return to Russia

This time, it was different. When my wife Betty and I first visited Russia, beautiful homeland of peasants and Czars and Tolstoy and Tchaikovsky, it was on the river cruise in the height of summer 1997. The sun beat down relentlessly as we sailed from St. Petersburg on the Baltic, across Lake Ladoga, and on down to the mighty Volga and Moscow. That was a heart-warming and long dreamed of experience – to visit the towns and cities, and more importantly, the villages and country homes of the ordinary Russian citizens. Such was the beauty of the Russian landscape – rolling meadows, never-ending forests, majestic rivers, splendid palaces and churches with their astonishing cupolas, the generosity and kindness of the people, we vowed we would someday return to Russia. We did. In a completely different way, and sooner than we had anticipated.

During our first trip, in the stop-over at Irma, in the heart of the Russian countryside, we'd met and made friends with the young schoolteacher, Angelique Savuskna Leodvina, who lived in the industrial town of Cherepovets. For the next four years I corresponded regularly with Angelique. I spoke a little Russian, but the written language was beyond me. Angelique was in a similar situation with English. But she had a good friend, Irina, who helped translate our letters and became my good friend in the process of doing so. After a year's hard work and much difficulty with visas, we managed to bring Angelique to Northern Ireland for a two week holiday. That was a wonderful time for us, but more especially for her. During one of our many conversations I mentioned to Angelique that the next time we visited Russia I'd like it to be in the extremity of a Russian winter, and to live with an ordinary Russian family, experiencing every day life as they lived it. Two or three months after Angelique returned home we received a letter from her. "Hugh! Betty! Come to visit us in February. It will be winter. Beautiful snow everywhere! You will stay in our home. Let us know the date you will come!"

Flattery and idle talk and loose invitations which are not meant to be accepted are not part of the Russian make-up. They tell it as it is – good, bad or indifferent. When I protested I hadn't thought of returning to Russia just yet, Angelique would have none of it. "Come now!" she reiterated in the next letter. "Everything is prepared for you! You will stay in my mother's flat. She has two rooms. And please! Bring edible seaweed!"

I had no idea what Angelique had been preparing for us. But I knew what she meant by edible seaweed. Dulse. We'd bought Angelique a couple of bags one day when we took her to Donaghadee. She loved it – couldn't get enough of it – and wanted more. Russians, particularly rural Russians, are big on natural products and food, Most of their clothes are made from natural materials. In summer they grow as many vegetables and fruit as they can, freezing and preserving and storing the food to see them through the long hard winter when fresh food is hard to come by. Their food is the natural product, not processed rubbish, dyed with all the colours of the rainbow and devoid of practically any nourishment. Mushrooms are a big favourite. I thought I knew the taste of mushrooms. Until I sampled Russian mushrooms, hand-picked, straight from the forest, an explosion of taste and flavour and smell, bearing no resemblance to the pathetically lifeless product we buy in our supermarkets. We loaded up with dulse. And with gifts, not only from ourselves, but also from the many friends Angelique had made during her stay with us, and from many other kind folk who'd never met her, but who wanted to share with the Russian people in any way they could. Many local shopkeepers in our town of Newtownards, hearing of our trip to visit Russian friends, generously plied us with more gifts to pass on. I refrain from mentioning the names of these generous souls only because demands might be made upon them to repeat what were simply spontaneous gestures of goodwill. But they know their kindness was much appreciated with grateful hearts by each recipient in Russia.

We flew out from Heathrow, Moscow bound, at lunchtime on February 18th, 2002, due to touch down at Sheremetevo airport at about 8:40pm Russian time, and to something of a dilemma. Cherepovets lies about four hundred miles from Moscow, in a slightly south easterly direction. Angelique is meticulous in every plan she sets her hand to. She would meet us at the airport. The original plan was to travel on to Cherepovets by overnight train, arriving early in the morning. But something had gone wrong. A day before our departure from Northern Ireland Angelique informed us she couldn't get train tickets for the journey. I was to learn that's the way it is in Russia. One day everything is possible. Next day nothing is possible. It doesn't bother the Russian. It has ever been so. He just works his way around the problem, and usually achieves his aim, whatever it may be. So it was now. We would travel the four hundred miles from Moscow to Cherepovets, through the Russian winter night, in a "kind of jeep!" I had no idea what Angelique meant by "a kind of jeep." But it didn't bother us. It simply added to the mystery and adventure and intrigue. If we'd wanted a luxury holiday, being "lifted and laid", we'd have booked it from one of the glossy brochures. Russia! In winter! Warts and all! To experience the Russian way of life as it came, good, bad or indifferent. That's what we wanted. Bring on the "kind of jeep!"

I was a little disappointed at the "kind of jeep". After clearing

Russian customs without a hitch (except that I still can't get any Russian official to smile at me) we exchanged warm hugs and kisses with the lovely Angelique who was suitably attired for the bitter Moscow weather in heavy fur coat and boots and hat. Angelique introduced us to Sasha, a small smiling man of about thirty or forty years of age. Sasha would drive "the kind of jeep" through the night. Sasha shook hands warmly, offered us a cigarette, which we declined, and led us to the car park. I expected the "kind of jeep" to be a ramshackle collection of bits and pieces on (hopefully) four wheels. It was with some surprise we were steered over to a very modern and comfortable Honda vehicle. Russian myth number one blown clean out of the water. I found out later Angelique had traded several days tutoring Anya, a factory executive's child, whom we would later meet, for the loan of the Honda.

Sasha loaded up the luggage. We climbed aboard and partook of the oranges and apples and pure fruit juice Angelique offered us as we commenced our journey across snowy Moscow. Soon the environs of the modern city gave way to the broad road leading to Cherepovets. All roads in Russia are extremely wide. There's plenty of room. But there is little or nothing in the way of road markings or lane division and even the sides of the road simply fall away into the fields or forests through which they have been hacked. I settled down in the front seat beside Sasha as he put his foot down and fairly belted along the straight never-ending road. Thick snowflakes swirled against the windscreen almost hypnotizing me as the wipers slapped noisily and keeping me in a conscious state. I expected Sasha to slow as visibility and conditions worsened. He didn't. Neither did the other traffic – lorries, cars, vans and army trucks – flashing past on the other side of the road with a perfect disdain for the conditions in which they were travelling. If this had been Britain the roads would have been deemed impassable, the weather so severe drivers everywhere advised not to venture out. I mentioned this to Sasha. He shrugged his shoulders as Russians always do when confronted with any sort of problem. "This Russia. If we stop driving or not travel, because of little snow, we sit home six months of year." I nodded. The weather, whatever it was, was just another problem. To be overcome.

I half closed my eyes as we hurtled into the white wilderness and the dense forests of snow-clad birch and fir trees spreading away for hundreds of miles on either side of the road. In my mind I recalled many happy hours at my own fireside, reading Tolstoy, and of the fantastic journeys many of his characters made on wild winter nights such as this – perhaps even through this very countryside, in their *troikas.* Now I too was travelling through that dark and snowy land, by night, through the birches and the pines, faster and faster and faster – even faster than Tolstoy's characters. But I was at one with them in their journeys, and what I saw around me would have been little different from what they had experienced. I was privileged. Even this journey, a supposed hardship for us because there was no train, was becoming a perhaps unique experience I would always remember.

A couple of hundred miles along the road Sasha pulled into the ditch and switched off the engine. Betty and Angelique were asleep in the back seat. Sasha pulled a packet of cigarettes from the glove-box and motioned to my door. I didn't smoke, but I was grateful for the opportunity to stretch my legs. There wasn't any traffic now. Only Sasha and myself, standing alone in the bitter cold of the beautiful Russian night in the barren snow-covered countryside, without a house or building of any sort, in any direction. Oh! The joy of unrestricted space and silence and utter loneliness on that freezing night as the snow ceased and a bright crescent moon shone down. Fifty miles or so farther along we stopped again at a little roadhouse for some coffee and *bleeni* – Russian pancakes – before setting out on the last part of the journey.

It was four o'clock in the morning and still dark when we arrived in Cherepovets. The snow began to fall again as Sasha steered through the modern city of high-rise flats and factories and eventually turned into a quiet courtyard which housed yet another block of flats. We had arrived. Sasha hauled our bags of luggage and gifts from the car and I lugged them over to the door of the flats. I pulled out my camera. It's important to record moments or faces which one might not experience again. Sasha had been a superb driver and a good companion, and a man of some modesty. He didn't consider himself worthy of any praise for his long night time drive and couldn't imagine why I'd want to take his photograph. Finally, at my insistence, he posed sheepishly beside the jeep. We took his photograph and hugged him goodbye. But not before we gave him a "*padarak*" – gift – a bottle of Irish whisky. Sasha said he was going home to sleep all day. Maybe the whisky would help him slip off to dreamland.

"Mother's flat on fourth floor," Angelique informed us. "We go!" I was looking forward to meeting Galena, Angelique's mother. I wasn't particularly happy at invading her household at four o'clock in the morning. The flights of stairs which gave access to the flat were similar to the housing estate flats in our own town, and without too much in the way of lighting. As I climbed the dark stairs with doors opening off everywhere I thought of the dwelling place of Raskolnikoff in Dostoevsky's *Crime and Punishment.* Like the night time journey through the Russian countryside, the experience was pleasing to me.

There are two entrance doors to every Russian flat, one immediately behind the other. Whether this is a form of double-glazing or a security feature, I am not sure. The inner door of Galena's flat was steel. As I became accustomed to closing it behind me when entering and leaving during the next two weeks I realised it would be impossible to force an entry through the door. The flat did not have a rear exit, or, as far as I could see, a fire escape. But there was a balcony, so maybe an exit stairway ran from it.

Angelique's mother, a wiry fair-haired pretty lady in her fifties, threw her arms around us and gave us a wonderfully warm welcome in a gush of pure Russian with the odd word of meaningless English tossed in for good measure. We already knew all

Russians treat any guest with honour and with all the hospitality and kindness they can muster. We were humbled to be invited into the home of this dear lady whom we had never met or even communicated with, and yet who was pleased to open her house to us for two weeks. We were friends immediately.

Westerners could learn many things from the Russian people. One of the simplest is their habit of removing their shoes immediately upon entering the home, moving around only in stocking feet. It's not a religious custom. It's a very practical one. Naturally, in winter, the Russian's boots and shoes are heavy with snow and need to be removed. But even in summer the same custom applies. Angelique, though saying nothing when she stayed with us in Newtownards, told all her friends when she returned home that the Northern Ireland people, including guests, walked about the house in the same shoes as they trod the streets. It is unheard of to wear footwear that has been in the streets, no matter how clean, inside the Russian home. Betty and I have adopted the Russian custom.

Galena's flat consisted of a modest bedroom, lounge, kitchen and bathroom, similar in size or perhaps slightly smaller than a Housing Executive flat. Simply decorated, warm and comfortable, we were at our ease immediately. We would sleep on the sofa-bed in the lounge, with Vaska, Galena's cat for company. I was more than ready to fall into the sofa-bed. But I had reckoned without the flood of Russian hospitality we experienced everywhere during our stay. Galena had already spread the table, despite the lateness – or earliness of the hour – with cheese, all sorts of meats, black and white breads, pastries, fruits, sweets, jams, chocolates, (Russians love chocolate!) and a couple of bottles of vodka. I eyed the vodka with some trepidation, remembering our previous visit to Russia. I knew I'd have to 'pass myself' on more than one occasion with the Russian firewater. And so it was. We tucked into the delicious food and laughed and joked as best we could in our two conflicting languages with me attempting a little Russian and Angelique doing a little better in English,

Galena rattling away in one hundred per cent pure Russian and Betty only opening her mouth to smile and nod as she did justice to the Russian delicacies and the vodka. Finally, despite Galena's protestations we eat and drink more, the table was cleared. After many more hugs and kisses, Galena and Angelique bade us good night. "Sleep long," smiled Angelique, a very practical girl. "Tomorrow you will rest." We were to discover this was to be about the only time Angelique would give us the opportunity of rest. She had prepared for us a holiday cram-packed with many different experiences of Russian life and hospitality which we would come to remember as among the most heart-warming and rewarding two weeks of our lives. After this, there would be little sleep. And little rest. Angelique promised "Every minute of your time will be filled with places to go. And things to do!"

We awoke at noon. I drew back the curtains and gazed down at the citizens coming and going in the snow-covered courtyard below and the flow of traffic on the main street beyond. No one hurried. Every citizen and every driver appeared to have all the time in the world to get to his or her destination, in marked contrast to the hurry and anxious bustle which abounds in the West. Over and over again I was to witness this lack of haste. Whatever the journey for the Russian citizen, short or long, it becomes part of the enjoyment of life and pleasure of the day. It is not to be hurried.

Galena and Angelique prepared us a delicious breakfast utilizing cheese, eggs, oatmeal, cucumbers, fruit, black bread, berries, sour cream and fresh fruit juices. Simple ingredients, but prepared and presented in unique Russian style and taste. I quickly discovered the value everything has for the Russian when I dipped the tea-bag on my saucer into my cup of hot water. I don't like strong tea. I gave the bag a couple of swirls and was about to dispose of it when Galena intervened. "*Nyet*!" she exclaimed. "*Nyet*!" She took the dripping tea-bag from me and pointed to her own and Angelique's cup. If I had finished with mine, it wouldn't be necessary to use their tea-bags. One would suffice for all three cups. The Russian wastes nothing. Can't afford to.

After breakfast we spent the afternoon unpacking and enjoying the pleasure and delight on the faces of our hosts as we presented them with gifts of clothes and perfumes and toiletries, including many items Angelique had admired when she visited us but was unable to transport back to Russia. The day was spent resting (and eating and drinking!) playing with Vaska the crazy cat, getting to know our surroundings and trying to communicate better with Galena. Then the usual feast which is the Russian supper in the evening with many toasts to each other and to our respective countries. It was late when we retired to the sofa-bed. But Angelique warned us. "Sleep well! From tomorrow it will be go, go, go for the rest of your holiday. Much to see. Much to do. There are many surprises for you!"

A few weeks before departing for Russia I had accepted invitations to speak at two schools in Cherepovets, School 21 and School 42. I had spoken to Mrs Carol Mayberry, Principal of my old school, Ballyvester Primary. Would Ballyvester be interested in sending greetings and establishing contact with the Russian schools? They would. The Ballyvester pupils prepared two booklets giving information about their school and themselves and the way of life in Northern Ireland. Now, after a good night's sleep, and a hearty Russian breakfast, Betty and I set out with Angelique to visit School 21. "Hugh! You are already very famous in School 21," laughed Angelique we trudged through the snow to the bus-stop where we'd meet our friend Irina who had set up the arrangements with both schools. "The students have read your stories and heard recordings of your broadcasts. They are very honoured and excited you agree to visit them!" I wasn't too sure they might be in for a disappointment – a writer from Newtownards coming to the land of Tolstoy and Dostoevsky to read and discuss his own work. If anyone was being honoured around here, it was me.

Much has been written about Russian queues. At the bus-stop quite a few people waited for the bus – pronounced "*avtoboos*" in Russian – but certainly not in any sort of order. They hung about all over the place. The bus, old, noisy and mud-splattered from the snowy streets pulled in a few feet away from us.

"Go! Go! Go!" shouted Angelique as she pushed Betty forward and up the steps. I hung back in deference to the passengers who had been there before I had. "Go! Go! Go!!" shouted Angelique giving me a push in the back.

I quickly learned no one stands on ceremony when it's time to board a bus in Russia. It's irrelevant whether you've been waiting thirty minutes or thirty seconds. It's every man, woman or child for himself, pushing and shoving and elbowing their way on board. But nobody takes offence. That's just the way it is. The bus is always packed to the gunnels, all seats taken, and every square inch of standing space absolutely filled. It's impossible to move on a Russian bus. How the conductress, who, being in uniform, rarely smiled, managed to move up and down to collect the fare – about four pence whatever your destination – is still a mystery to me. I held on tightly as the driver, with passengers sitting almost on top of him, turned up the volume of his transistor, slammed the bus into gear and roared away. No one expects any degree of comfort or style on an *avtoboos.* It's just something which gets you from A to B. Why fuss or get uptight?

I was impressed with School 21, a large spacious building which oozed character. We were warmly greeted at reception then taken to the staff-room to ease off our heavy overcoats and boots and hats. After we'd made ourselves presentable we were escorted through the bright and tidy corridors toward the Assembly Room where I was assured the enthusiastic pupils were waiting with baited breath to meet "the famous writer from

Northern Ireland!" Not quite sure I could live up to this billing, the pressure mounted when a television crew pounced on me just outside the Assembly Room. Could I spare a moment to do an interview? That was the first of two television, one radio, and one press interview I did during the next two weeks. If you're a struggling author, pop over to Russia for a couple of weeks! Writers are held in great esteem in that country.

Betty and I were given a very warm ovation from the forty or so students as we entered the large room and were escorted to the guest-table at the front of the audience. A beautiful teenage female student in Russian national costume welcomed us on behalf of her school and invited us to partake of the customary loaf of bread and salt which is typical Russian hospitality given to all travellers. Although I had encountered this lovely custom on our previous Russian travels I was deeply moved as I broke a piece from the loaf and dipped it in the salt before slipping it into my mouth. All Russian traditions are simple. I suppose this one may have been founded on the supposition a traveller may be hungry after his long journey. And in the old times salt was a precious commodity.

The television crew moved in to cover the action as we were welcomed again and told something of the work at the school. Then I was requested to do a fifteen minute question and answer spot for the pupils. I was struck by the intelligence, neatness, manners, enthusiasm and superb English of the students, aged, I guessed, from about fourteen to seventeen. The questions, including many about my writing career, were straight to the point. Did I write for fame? Or for money? Well, a little bit of fame or a little bit of money doesn't go amiss, I informed my audience. But I wrote primarily because there are many things in my heart I want to share with other people. That brought an immediate warm round of applause. The students had already read my account of our first visit to Russia, published in 1997, and thanked me for speaking so well of their country and its people. They'd also read many of my stories and heard tapes of my BBC radio broadcasts. The students were keen to know how Russia was viewed by the West, and my opinion of Cherepovets. After I'd provided this information I was told that the students had adapted one of my stories *The Happiest Christmas of All* into a play. They would be honoured if I would take the part of the father of the two children and act out a scene which they had rehearsed for my visit. They would be honoured? Nothing to the honour I felt at that moment that these dear people should think enough of my work to adapt and perform it, in period costume, complete with a beautiful dance sequence. I'm an emotional old so and so. Tears filled my eyes at the very thought of Russian children presenting my work on a Russian stage. But then tears were never far away during the entire two weeks. The Russian citizens, for whom life is not always easy, are among the kindest and most warm-hearted people I have ever met.

When the performance ended the students entertained us with lovely performances of Russian songs and dances. The songs included two of my favourites, *Greenfields* and the beautiful *Moscow Nights*. At the finish another emotional few moments when we were presented with many beautiful gifts of Russian craft and art work. My gifts to School 21 were simple – greetings and personal details of pupils at Ballyvester School, a Northern Ireland calendar, a shillelagh, (which intrigued everyone) and an Irish leprechaun named Finnigen. Finnigen got the biggest cheer of the afternoon. I was then given a folder giving personal details of the School 21 students to pass on to Ballyvester, or to anyone who would like to make contact. Then I was besieged with a Russian 'queue' of students politely asking for my autograph.

After the students returned to their classes clutching the autographs we were royally entertained with *chi* and a huge pile of *bleeni*, an in-depth discussion about Northern Ireland and Russia, and afterwards a tour of the lovely school. I came away from the college humbled. Students and teachers have little in the way of facilities or salaries – some teachers working free to educate the children. Perhaps we have much to learn from both in the manner in which they apply themselves to learning and to teaching. Student and teacher work in harmony. For the Russian student, learning is not a chore, a necessary bore. It is a joyful and uplifting experience. We took our leave of School 21, wiser than when we'd gone in, humbled by the warmth of the reception and sorry we had to leave a place of learning where pupils consider it a privilege to be taught, and teachers an honour to teach.

Back at Galena's flat we rested until early evening when Galena challenged me to a game of chess. Russian chess players are the best in the world, and I'd already seen some of Galena's winner's plaques. It was with some trepidation I sat down to face the local champion.

I still can't understand it. Maybe Galena had an off night. Or maybe she bestowed upon me typical Russian courtesy and good manners. I won. Maybe these Russian chess players aren't all they're cracked up to be, I thought, as I cleared away the board and Galena and Angelique began to lay the table for supper.

Supper! Russians are big on salads – they grow all their own vegetables and fruit on their little patch of ground – maybe on the other side of town – then preserve or bottle them any way they can to see them through the winter. Food appeared from everywhere – from under the window frames, from hidden cupboards, out on the freezing balcony, (excellent fridge!) and from bottles and boxes. Meats of every description, eggs, red cabbage, pickled cucumbers, fish, cheese, black and white bread, *borsch* soup, (my favourite) berries and umpteen other things I'd never seen before. Bottles of wine. And vodka. Always vodka, which I was instructed to knock back in one go, despite being a tee-totaller. I obeyed. When I came back down from the ceiling Galena crammed my mouth with the Russian antidote, a brimming spoonful of sugar. It hadn't worked when we'd been in old Anastasia's shack in Irma a few years earlier. It didn't work now. After supper Galena switched on the television to watch the news. There we were on prime-time Russian television, being interviewed at School 21 and enjoying what had been a most up-lifting experience. It's difficult to put into words our feelings that evening as Galena helped us open up our sofa-bed. I select one. It does the best job. Humbled. We were humbled that these two Russian ladies, mother and daughter, should welcome us into their modest little home – not only as guests, but as friends – and spare no thought or effort to ensure our comfort. Through the years, writing has brought me a few accolades. I've wined and dined with a few top people in a few top places. But nothing has ever given me a greater sense of kindness and love and fellowship and feeling of being at one with my fellow human-being as when I turned in for the night in the home of these two lovely Russian ladies.

Next morning after breakfast we struggled into winter coats and boots. Angelique was taking us for a visit to the Cherepovets Museum. At the museum Angelique introduced us to the two young ladies who would guide us round. Galena (same name as Angelique's mother) and Lidiya, both students, were a mine of information about the museum, which itself was really a history of Cherepovets. The amazing thing about Russians – any Russian – is their ability to relate practically every known fact about the place where they live, going back hundreds of years, and the history of the Russian nation as a whole. After the museum, Galena and Lidiya accompanied us to the home of one of Russia's most famous artists, Vasily Vereshchagin, probably best known for his Apotheosis of War painted in 1871. As we moved around the house, maintained almost as the artist had left it, I half-closed my eyes in an effort to suspend time and to travel back and be part of the building when Vereshchagin lived there. It is always a privilege to be in the space where a great artist or writer or composer worked, even if it is not possible to be there in their time.

When we'd exhausted the treasures of Vereshchagin's former home we tumbled out into the snow covered streets to be greeted by a bright sun and powder-blue sky. We walked by the river. It was about a mile wide and, as Angelique informed us, frozen solid to a depth of about six feet. The citizens of Cherepovets, like all Russians, turn every disadvantage to an advantage. The frozen river provided an excellent short-cut from one side of town to the other. Everything was a dazzle of pristine whiteness in the sunny afternoon – the frozen river, the fields beyond, and the banks of birch trees so beloved by the Russian. The birch is used to make shoes, hats, pictures, ornamental flowers, paper, and a hundred other items. It is the stuff of Russian songs, stories and poetry, and is loved just as much as the Volga, the river Russians affectionately term 'Mother Volga'. I don't think I ever experienced such stillness of heart and oneness with nature as I did during those two weeks we traversed the snow-covered Russian countryside with a far horizon, a wide sky and birch and pine trees ever near. I'm still homesick. For Russia.

Coming back into the town we visited a few souvenir shops. I was especially interested in the local artwork. A lot of it featured snow-drenched birch forests with onion-domed churches hiding in the background. It's always difficult for a foreigner to identify a shop in Russia. They don't usually have a large window, or any window, displaying their wares. Shops, indeed most public buildings, look just like an ordinary Russian house from the outside. If you know what you're doing and push open a door you may well enter the most resplendent historical home, a shop – of any type – or a dramatic museum. But everything in the souvenir shops was of excellent quality and almost everything was handmade. The exchange rate was about thirty *roubles* for our dollar. We soon found out we could be big-time spenders in Cherepovets!

After our wander around town we returned again to Galena and the flat. Like most Russians, Angelique's mother grabs life with both hands. Russians live life. To the full. Forget the glossy magazines, the kitchen of the year, the latest fashion you simply can't live without, the house on the hill, the car that does 0–100mph in thirty seconds, and satellite television with a hundred and fifty channels of drivel. Happily, the average Russian, like Galena, doesn't need them. Galena is in a chess group. She swims. She skis. She sings in a choral group. She dances. She walks in the forest. In short, she lives. And tonight Betty and I were to be the special guests of her choral group as they performed a selection of Russian favourites.

"Marvellous!," I exclaimed. "Will there be a big audience?"

"*Nyet*," replied Galena, through Angelique. "Six persons. You. Betty. Angelique, Irina, and Irina's two children Anton and Anastasia. Special performance. Just for you."

Russian songs and Russian music always move me to tears. In the beautiful old hall where the performance took place we were welcomed as honoured guests. Then Galena and her couple of dozen friends touched our hearts with songs of the Russian homeland – songs of sorrow and tragedy, of the Volga and the birch tree, and surprisingly enough, finishing with a tear-jerking version of Auld Lang Syne. At the close I addressed the assembled company and expressed our delight at the quality of the musical offering and thanked our hosts for a wonderful evening. Later we spoke as best we could with the performers individually. I knew many of the ladies and gentlemen wanted to communicate with us but couldn't because of the language barrier. The barrier collapsed as we hugged and kissed each other and tears slipped from every eye. Words are not always necessary to express what is in the heart. A warm handshake, a hug, a kiss, can do it just as well. Perhaps better. And again, these dear people believed we had honoured them with our presence. But it was we who were honoured. Galena's friend Lydia, one of the performers, journeyed back through the dark snowy streets with us to Galena's flat where another excellent supper was served. After we'd enjoyed the meal Lydia and Galena sang happily – and sadly – of the Russian homeland, and we all danced and sang, Russian style. When Lydia donned her street-shoes and left to go home the redoubtable Galena challenged me to another game of chess.

Galena destroyed me in a few swift moves. There remained no further doubt in my mind she had taken a dive in the first game. I congratulated her on her skills as she smiled broadly and helped us pull out the sofa-bed. Tomorrow would be another busy and interesting day, commencing with a visit to School 42 where Anton and Anastasia, the children of our interpreter were educated. I was asleep before my head hit the pillow.

Betty and I had the distinct honour of being the first foreign guests ever to visit School 42. Again I sensed the great air of dignity and pride and respect and appreciation children and teachers had for the place of learning. Many of the teachers informed me they had been taught here themselves. There was no mistaking the privilege they felt they enjoyed in being able to pass their knowledge on to others. It was a pleasure for me to respond to the children's informed questioning and enjoy their beautiful singing and dancing. One young male teenager, immaculately groomed, came forward and recited, in perfect English, Byron's "Twilight." The schoolchildren recited English poetry, sang songs of the classical composers, and enquired of us foreigners about life in our native land. Even at their tender age, I was aware their education exceeded mine. I was invited to read one of my Christmas stories, *The Most Beautiful Christmas Tree of All.* It appeared to be one of the school's favourite stories. At the finish I was again besieged for autographs. Later, as we toured the rest of the beautiful school I commented on the curtains on the windows and the flowers and plants which decorated each classroom.

"These aren't like classrooms," I commented to one teacher. "They're more like living-rooms at home."

The teacher smiled. "Thank you," she replied in perfect English. "This is what we try to do. Make the children feel comfortable, just as if they were at home. Learning should be a joyful and happy experience. We try to make it so." I nodded, remembering my latter days at the Newtownards Technical School when Mr Wally Brown and Mr Spud Murphy used to knock our blocks off. The clouts on the head never did us any harm. But it was certainly a different approach from the Russian system of education.

We departed from School 42, clutching gifts and good wishes and reams of addresses from students seeking to make contacts in Northern Ireland. Again, we wondered at the application of children to whom the whole realm of education was not a tiresome duty but an exciting and pleasurable privilege.

The rest of the day was spent wandering around the street-markets which weren't unlike those at home. I bought a bottle of after-shave which Angelique assured me was "genuine Moscow quality". Betty bought some baby-clothes for our forthcoming great-grandchild.

Later that evening we togged up in our best gear. Angelique instructed us it had to be our best. She was taking us to a concert – a very special concert – and Angelique had assumed wardrobe approval for the evening. She rummaged through our clothes, discarding this and that, and indicating we should wear only the very best of our garments for this occasion. All decked up like something out of a club-book, we set out again, crunching through the snow to wait on the faithful old *avtoboos* which soon landed us at a magnificent theatre on the other side of town. All Russian theatres are works of art. This one was no exception. We hurried up the broad marble steps and into the deeply carpeted foyer which in itself was larger than some theatres over here. I was slightly uneasy. Angelique, who always had everything organized to the smallest detail, didn't display her usual confidence. And she didn't seem to have tickets for the performance, nor any indication she was about to purchase any. The place teemed with soldiers of the Red Army, every one sporting half a dozen rows of campaign medals on his tunic breast.

"Wait here!," commanded Angelique as she took off into the crowd of the aforementioned military might. In about two minutes she returned on the arm of an elderly silver-haired gentleman sporting enough brass and gongs to leave me in no doubt this was the General of the Red Army. He beamed at Betty and myself.

"Good evening," he bowed. "Please follow me!" We did,

through the chasm which opened up in the crowd as the General swept forward and into the most magnificent theatre I've ever seen. The place was already packed with military officers. But the General escorted us to three top-notch seats, centre front. He smiled, bowed, and left us. I sat down, not at all sure Angelique hadn't got the wrong theatre. I sneaked a look at the gentleman beside me. Another General, with even more medals than our late host. I waited to feel the firm grip of the KGB on the back of my neck. What were we doing here among all this top-ranking army personnel?

Angelique leaned over. "This is Soldiers Day," she whispered. "A holiday in all Russia. The concert is special. Only for the defenders of our Motherland and their families." I nodded. How Angelique had managed to get us in, without tickets, and escorted to the best seats in the house by a top-ranking General, was beyond me. But that was typically Angelique. She had contacts everywhere, from street-cleaners to the top of the Red Army. Later we would travel four hundred miles east to Veliki Ustiug and then north several hundred miles to Moscow. She had contacts there. Shopkeepers, company directors, street urchins. She knew everybody. Was it something to do with the Russian system of bartering for favours needed? Angelique was a schoolteacher and wasn't above giving a few hours teaching to any person or their offspring in exchange for something she herself needed. The house lights dimmed. The concert was preceded by many speeches from many military people, and by the Mayor of Cherepovets who just happened to be seated beside Angelique and Betty. The concert was a spectacular success – a blend of typical Russian national fervour, folk-dancing, singing, ballet, chorus, circus and drama all rolled into one. I never miss an opportunity to see any Russian performance. It's always full of passion and fire and pathos, and always worth at least twice the admission money, whatever it might be.

When the concert ended we relaxed in the marble-walled ante-rooms with the military might of Russia and their friends.

Betty has a thing about Russian soldiers. The last time we were in Moscow, in Red Square, she accosted one fine specimen with whom she elected to have her photograph taken. This time it was four bemused soldiers who didn't know whether to smile or run as Betty planted herself between them and instructed me to click the camera. Photographing Russian soldiers! In Russia! Time was we'd have ended up in Siberia for doing that!

And so another delightful evening drew to a close, finished off with a leisurely walk home and a lovely little meal prepared by cook par excellence Angelique in Galena's flat. And another game of chess. Galena, confidence high after her annihilation of me in the previous game, threw down the gauntlet once again. Surprisingly, I just edged her in a tightly fought match. I was pleasantly surprised. 2–1 to the Newtownards man. And that's how the series ended. We packed so much into the remainder of the holiday there simply wasn't time for another game.

"Sleep well", smiled Angelique as we prepared to retire for the night. "Tomorrow we go to the country!"

Most Northern Ireland folk suffer from the "shop-'til-you-drop" syndrome. Not so the Russian citizens. The mind-numbing disease of consumerism has no place in their lives. On Saturday morning, at first light, when I knew the population of Northern Ireland would be pouring into the towns for a spending spree, the citizens of Cherepovets were headed the other way. Out to the country. Russians love every aspect of nature. At weekends they can't wait to throw off the shackles of the town and get to the fields and forests and rivers. And they are by no means disadvantaged in winter. Everybody, children, parents, grandparents, aunts, uncles – everyone heads to the snow – covered country side and the hilly forests. To ski. Droves of them, carrying their skis upright, wrapped up in warm jackets and gloves and trousers and ski-hats, laughing and slipping and sliding on their way to the faithful *avtoboos* which would take them out to the country.

A bright winter sun blazed from a spectacularly blue sky as Betty and I tramped along with Galena, Angelique, Irina, Anton and Anastasia, and Anya, daughter of the managing director of a local factory whom I found out later had laid on the jeep which had brought us from Moscow to Cherepovets. I noted the excitement and happiness on every face as they piled aboard the bus, carrying their skis with such dexterity they never seemed to get in anyone's way.

Any Russian landscape is breath-taking. But I gasped at the majesty of the winter scene before me as we alighted from the bus. A wide open expanse of snow as far as I could see, fringed by distant birch and pines on the horizon. Off to our right, a little knot of woods and hills in which skiers of all ages were already testing their skills. But it wasn't a formal affair. Everybody was just having fun – skiing, playing in the snow, riding the snowmobile, knocking back vodka or iced-tea and cream cakes in the little wooden cabin-cum-cafe. And singing. On a makeshift stage near the start and finish of the ski races. I was invited to sing. Perhaps I may have one or two little talents. Singing is not one of them. I have never, at any time, in any place, allowed myself to be coaxed into song. Apart from having to hit the correct note, you have to remember the correct words, hopefully in the correct order. But when my Russian friends invited me to warble, I had no hesitation in accepting. Before I even knew what I would sing I stood up, opened my mouth, not knowing what was going to come out. I found out, at exactly the same time as my Russian audience, it would be *Danny Boy*. It seemed to go down quite well. A genuine round of applause swept the sun-lit glade, probably more in appreciation of my courage than ability. But they dressed me up in the Russian sporting colours and pushed me up on the ski winners podium. In Russian eyes, I was a winner!

Late that afternoon we were invited to the home of Sergi, the gentleman who loaned the jeep, his wife Irina and daughter

Anya. Their flat was beautifully furnished in the very best of taste. It was obvious this was a family of some means. Our hosts were delightful but didn't have any English, except for Anya who was beginning to learn it at school. I was really pushed to make myself understood in my poor Russian. But again we found language no barrier when people of like mind meet. We enjoyed a spectacular dinner – the vodka and wine flowing like water as usual – and examined many of Anya's works of art. The young girl asked us which of her paintings we liked best. Betty and I both indicated a painting. Anya reached it to Betty. "For you," she said simply. "*Padarak.*" That was typical of the generous Russian heart. Not only did Anya hand over her artwork but also her favourite collection of sea-shells she had collected when on holiday at the Black Sea. And Betty was given a beautiful stole which she had admired and which Anya's grandmother had knit from goats wool. Me? I got a bottle of the best – the very best – Russian vodka.

"*Spasseba bolohoi*!" I smiled as Sergi handed it to me. "We will take a drink from it every Christmas to remind us of you and our happy time in your home."

"Every Christmas!" repeated Sergi incredulously as Angelique translated. "Every Christmas! When we open vodka, bottle finish same night!"

We departed from our lovely guests to accept another invitation to dinner. This time in the home Zoha, the mother of the other Irina, who was our translator and friend. Zoha was elderly, a large warm lady, and typically Russian. She embraced us with open arms and open heart and many kisses. It was evident we were more than welcome in her comfortable little home. I think we were all there that evening. Yura – Irina's husband, the children Anton and Anastasia, Galena, Angelique and ourselves. And what a beautiful feast Zoha had prepared, dominated by a huge fishpie which almost filled the table. The cranberry juice, made by Zoha from freshly picked berries, was delicious, and packed with genuine flavour. Again there wasn't any shortage of vodka. It really was hard work trying to do justice to Zoha's table immediately after the splendid meal we'd enjoyed at Sergi's. But we did our best. After dinner Angelique played the piano while we handed out gifts from ourselves and from kind friends in Northern Ireland. Zoha presented Betty and I with three large and lavishly decorated wooden Russian bowls, complete with wooden spoons. In the West the wooden spoon is something of no value. The Russian wooden spoon is a work of art. We had a happy, happy evening, to bring to a close another full and very beautiful day, made all the richer by the company of more newly found friends who would always remain very dear to us.

We slept well, head to toe as usual on the old sofa-bed. When I awoke next morning I was a year older. It was my birthday. Sergi, Anya's father, arrived after breakfast to fulfil a promise to take us on a guided tour of his fertilizer factory which was one of the largest in Russia. Sergi drove us to the plant on the edge of town in his Zhiguli – better known in Britain as the Lada – through a snow blizzard. Much of the tour included clambering up exterior iron staircases maybe twenty storeys high while the blizzard raged around us. Betty, who gets vertigo if she puts on a pair on high heels, found it tough going. But she battled on. At one point inside the plant we stood beside a pile of one thousand tons of white salt-like chemical heaped high like a mountain of snow. I didn't know what it was. But the smell of it stung my nose and made my eyes weep profusely. I was glad when we moved away from it. The entire production of Sergi's factory is transported by train to St. Petersburg and exported to Cuba. It's a big money-spinner for the Russian economy. Apart from the manufacturing areas Sergi proudly showed us the control room and the computers which monitor every part of the production. When we finally left Sergi pointed to the man with the shovel who was trying to keep the main entrance clear of snow, close to where we'd seen the mountain of white chemical. Sergi was pleased to inform us the man was permitted to retire five years before anyone else because of his proximity to the chemical mountain and the health problems it posed. I tried not to breath in as I reckoned the man might have been better off shovelling snow in some other part of Russia, even if he did have to do it for an extra five years.

After the factory visit our translator friend Irina invited us to her home for lunch with her husband Yura and the two children Anton and Anastasia. Luba, one of the teachers from School 21 would also be there. Irina and Luba worked away preparing a typically delicious Russian lunch while Yura and I discussed matters theological and ecological. Yura's dream is to take up his government's offer of two hectares of land somewhere out in the remote countryside and build a cabin where he and his family can live in close harmony with nature. Yura and Irina, despite living in a town of heavy manufacturing, are extremely close to nature in their outlook. They want to teach their children what is really important about life and living, and that the natural riches of the planet they live on are not inexhaustible. It takes wisdom and courage and sacrifice to do that. I hope it works out for these kind people. They deserve it. Irina is very much in tune, not only with the natural world, but with the needs of her fellow-man. I recall one particular incident somewhere in town which really brought this home to me. As we all dashed to board a bus a man on crutches fell to the ground and couldn't get up. I saw him. So did Irina. It's every man for himself when boarding a bus or train in Russia. Angelique hadn't seen the man fall and was shouting in my ear "Go! Go! Go!" I hesitated. I wanted to help the man. As the other passengers piled on to the bus I tried to establish in my mind if the man was drunk, whether I'd be able to help him, or if I'd be left stranded and alone as the bus roared away with everyone else safely aboard. Irina, oblivious to everything else, ran back and helped the man to his feet. She picked up his crutches and helped him on to the bus. She didn't stopped to consider what was best for her. Only what was best for the stricken man. I hung my head in shame.

In the afternoon, after the delicious lunch in Irina's flat, Angelique informed us she would take us all for a tour of the local folk museum. The museum was a large building housing many crafts and artifices of Russian life as it once was. It also contained a most interesting shop where one could purchase some of the superbly worked pieces of art. I indicated I would like to make some purchases.

"*Nyet*! *Nyet*! Later!" exclaimed Angelique. She quickly shoved me and the rest of our group through a large doorway into a very spacious hall. I was surprised to see about forty people, dressed in their best, sitting around a number of large tables which held enough food to feed half of Russia. They burst into spontaneous applause as we made our entrance. I realized immediately this was another of Angelique's surprises. A birthday party. For you know who.

That was a happy, emotional and wonderful evening, one of the most memorable occasions of my life. I could hardly believe it. A birthday party for me, in Russia, with maybe forty people I'd never met before. Galena was there and greeted me with her stock phrase of English she'd been learning since our arrival at her home – "Hello. Hugh. The sun is shining. It is a nice day!" It was dark outside and it was snowing. But I agreed wholeheartedly with Galena as I hugged her tightly. We were invited to take the seats of honour at the banqueting table. Practically every guest made a speech in my honour and I think everyone presented me with gifts of Russian arts and crafts and literature, each determined to outdo the other with their offerings. Some of the gifts were expensive. I could tell that. Some were inexpensive trifles. But for me each gift was of equal value. I understood the sacrifice each person would have made to secure it for me. I knew each offering came from an equally kind and generous heart. We dined like royalty. In between each course (in Russia it seems there are always about twenty courses) the gifts were presented.

And at a Russian party everyone delights to sing a song, dance, or play a piece of music. It comes naturally to them. Perhaps it's an escape from their hum-drum and often difficult life-style. But they just can't be restrained if there's an opportunity for a bit of a knees-up, and any excuse will do to have one. How my hosts let themselves go that night! Laughter, accordion playing, dancing, singing, tears, games, more laughter and then the beginning of the vodka toasts. My hosts toasted, individually, my birthday, Betty's birthday – which was five months away – our children, our children's children and our great-grandchildren which were yet to be born. My late parents, uncles, aunts, grandparents, the food, the tea, and finally the vodka itself was toasted. Anything and everything will serve as an excuse for a vodka toast in Russia. And when they've toasted everything they can possibly think of, they'll do it all over again. Angelique presented me with my birthday cards as Irina translated the sentiments on each one. One card was from the Mayor of Cherepovets. Another came from Russia's leading female popular singer, no doubt one of Angelique's mates.

It was a memorable joy to spend the evening with these wonderful people who take life as it comes, enjoy what they can, and make do with what is not particularly good. When the night finally ended we embraced our friends over and over again, hugging each other tightly, sharing our hearts. Finally, burdened down with our gifts, we shuffled out into the dark streets. We trudged back through the snowy streets to the *avtoboos* and Galena's flat. As we pulled out the sofa-bed Angelique smiled. "Good sleep, Hugh and Betty. Tomorrow we go on holiday!"

I was too exhausted to explain to Angelique. Obviously she was having a translation problem. I'd tell her in the morning. We were already on holiday.

Return to Russia II

In the morning we discovered Angelique did indeed intend to take us for a holiday within a holiday. "Pack bags," Angelique instructed us when we'd finished another whopping breakfast. "Many warm clothes. And good boots. You will need!"

"Where are we going?" I asked as we stuffed our travel bags with the warmest clothes we had.

"Veliki Ustiug," smiled Angelique. "Hugh! You always say you want to experience Russian winter. So. I take you to the land of Father Frost – the real Santa Claus. I take you to his home. Maybe we will even meet him!"

The real Santa Claus? Angelique was right. I wouldn't mind meeting up with him. "How far is it to where Father Frost lives?" I enquired. "Not far," laughed Angelique. "Only about seven hundred kilometres."

Seven hundred kilometres! So how long would it take to get there?

"Not long," replied Angelique in a matter of fact tone. "Only sixteen hours. By bus and overnight train. But hurry. First I wish to show you my flat. In it I have many of useful things I buy when I stay with you in Northern Ireland. I am very proud of my flat. And also, Galena say Cherepovets Boys Choir wish to sing specially for you this morning in their choral rooms. If you do them the honour to accept invitation mother Galena will take you there later."

A bus ride across town brought us to Angelique's flat in a typical high-rise building which is common to most Russian towns. The flat consisted of one fairly large room with living and dining and sleeping areas tastefully separated by curtains and dividers so one got the impression it was a three room flat. The bathroom, like the rest of the flat, was equal in style and quality to what would be normal in the West. Pride of place in Angelique's home went to a huge genuine Spanish mahogany cabinet. It was a superb piece of craftsmanship. Angelique will only have about her items which are of genuine quality. If she cannot afford to pay for them she will do without rather than buy cheap imitations. Like most Russians, surface glamour counts for little with Angelique. The workmanship must be genuine and made to last. The Russian does not, and could not afford to live in a throw-away society. And when Angelique had visited us the previous year she'd been greatly impressed by our pretty ordinary microwave.

"I have dream to own microwave," she'd enthused as she cooked us a splendid Russian meal in our own kitchen. "But in Russia, only rich people can afford. Maybe I save hard my *roubles.* I buy microwave!" Now, in her lovely little kitchen, Angelique pointed proudly to the realization of her dream. "See Betty! See Hugh. I have microwave!"

A ring on the door bell found Galena ready to take us back across town by bus to the Cherepovets Boys Choir. We were received in the choral rooms by Olga, a pretty red-haired lady I'd met at my birthday party and who had apparently issued the invitation to us. Olga showed us around the typically old but solid rambling building where the choir was based. The boys, informally dressed and ranging in age from about eight to twenty years of age, were obviously delighted to be performing for visitors from the West. Their repertoire and singing was of the highest quality – selections from Beethoven and Mozart – performed with ease and beauty and warmth. We congratulated the boys on their excellent performance and thanked them and presented them with a few souvenirs of Northern Ireland. Later, as we left the building, after much hospitality from our hosts, we spotted a few of the boys trudging through the snowy street. Normal lads – almost street urchins – yet so familiar with the music of the masters and an ability to interpret and perform it with great skill and sensitivity.

We returned to Galena's flat to pick up our bags. Then we headed to the railway station with Angelique to catch the train for Veliki Ustuig. Irina met us at the station. She would accompany Betty and Angelique and I on the long journey east to Veliki Ustiug and the land of Father Frost. We boarded the packed but comfortable train. Angelique said the first part of the journey would take two and a half hours and then we'd stop at the ancient town of Vologda. I was well aware of the sideways glances many of my fellow passengers shot at me during our train journey. Although we thought we didn't, one of our guides on our first Russian trip told us all Westerners stick out like a sore thumb to Russians. It needs to be remembered Russians are not at all used to seeing foreigners in the flesh, and especially Western foreigners. The self-conscious secretive glances from behind newspapers and handkerchiefs – and sometimes straight unashamed stares – were not meant to be offensive. We were simply the object of a deep curiosity. As we journeyed farther east the snow deepened and the unending forests of birch and pine became more and more dense until it seemed there was nothing left in the world but snow covered trees standing silent and still like a mighty army. I wanted to stop the train, step down and wander deep into the forests, build myself a hut, and live the rest of my days in peace and quiet and seclusion, secure in the knowledge no one would ever discover my existence. Angelique wasn't the only one with a dream! We stepped down from the train at the ancient Vologda railway station long after darkness had fallen. "Two and a half hours we wait for next train." explained Angelique. "What we do? Sit in waiting-room? Or see town of Vologda?" The voting was unanimous to see, by night, the old town with its snow-covered streets and cupola-topped churches, quiet and peaceful beneath a starry sky and a golden moon. The churches of Russia – even the smallest – are breathtaking in their beauty – simple, yet majestic. Angelique and Irina, although several hundred miles away from their hometown, related to Betty and I all the historical facts about Vologda. As we trudged through an almost deserted and dimly lit park we came to a huge bronze statue of a rider upon a horse.

"Who is this?" I asked Angelique. This time neither Angelique nor Irina appeared to have the answer. This bothered the pair of them, and especially Angelique. But help was close to hand when Angelique spotted a courting couple on a secluded park bench a few yards away. Angelique plunged through the snow and immediately engaged the love-birds in conversation. She returned after a few minutes and triumphantly gave us the history of horse and rider. I was amazed. Firstly that Angelique would be aware the courting-couple would certainly have the information required. Secondly, that she would have no hesitation in approaching them to obtain it. I couldn't see it happening in my hometown.

It was nine o'clock when we boarded the sleeper train which would take us to Yadriha. Irina informed us that when we reached Yadriha, in the morning, there would be another two hour journey through the wilderness by bus. We made ourselves comfortable in our carriage, or to be more accurate, our own part of the carriage. Our long bench seats could be adapted to make a comfortable enough bunk to sleep on, with two more bunks which opened up and were suspended from the ceiling. The train was warm, each carriage being heated by a sort of coal-burning stove which fed hot water around a channel of pipes. Angelique took off up the carriageway and returned with blankets and pillows which weren't included in the train fare, but which could be hired from the stewardess. The seats and sleeping area were not enclosed but open to the aisle running the length of the carriage. It didn't seem to bother the Russians. Male and female, strangers to each other, they did the best they could to strip off for a good night's sleep. A garment which slipped awkwardly at the wrong moment was no big deal to them. Unaccustomed as I am to undressing in full view of a selection of strangers, both male and female, I pretended it was no big deal to me either. Judging by the chuckles and knowing looks and nudges exchanged by Angelique and Irina, maybe I pretended a little too much. But eventually we all settled down. I stretched myself out on my bunk and pulled the blankets over my head. It wasn't long until my eyes grew heavy and I drifted off to sleep to the rhythm of the gently swaying train and the clickity-click of the wheels as we rolled farther and farther into the night. Another of my ambitions was being realized. I was journeying across Russia. Eastwards. By overnight train.

I slept soundly through the night as the train carried us farther and farther across Russia toward Veliki Ustuig and the home of Father Frost, the real Santa Claus. I arose early from my bunk. Excellent idea. No females awake to observe a difficult dressing in an open sleeping area. I glanced over at my wife Betty and our friends Angelique and Irina. Still asleep. Safe for me to rise and shine. I pulled on a shirt and trousers and a pair of socks and cautiously made my way to the back of the carriage where I hoped the stewardess would be slaving away over a hot samovar and a coffee machine. She was. In my best Russian I ordered one coffee without sugar, two coffees with milk and sugar, and one tea with lemon. I was pleased the stewardess seemed to understand me and that I'd carried it off so well. Russian isn't a difficult language to speak, though I did make a faux pas of monumental proportions a couple of nights earlier at the home of Angelique's mother, Galena. Galena had gone out somewhere and was very late in returning. As Irina and Angelique fussed about what may have happened, I decided I'd offer my opinion. In Russian. "Perhaps Galena is out on the street somewhere. Lost," I suggested. Angelique and Irina immediately collapsed on the floor in two heaps of hysterical laughter. Apparently I suggested Galena was somewhere down in the street giving birth to a baby elephant. Well, you have to try.....

I gently nudged my three companions awake. They rubbed the sleep from their eyes and accepted their mugs of coffee and tea, somewhat surprised I'd been able to procure it without any help. When Betty and Angelique and Irina finished their drinks I tactfully turned my head and gazed through the frosted carriage window to the pines beyond as the ladies struggled into their clothes. Once we were all decent we enjoyed a breakfast of cheese and apples and bread rolls we'd brought with us.

"Hurry!," encouraged Angelique as I chewed on my apple. "Soon we leave train." She was correct. Through the years I'd watched many television documentaries on the Russian way of life. I'd often wondered why trains always stopped in the middle of a barren and snow-covered countryside and the passengers disgorged and just wandered off, seemingly to be stranded for evermore, nowhere near a railway station. Now we did exactly the same thing. Angelique hustled us down from the carriage steps. We plunged almost knee deep into fresh sparkling snow. The sun shone brightly and the sky was clear and powder blue and seemed to stretch forever. My eyes followed the gleaming railway lines stretching away across the flat landscape as far as the eye could see in front of the engine, and glinting backwards across the hundreds of miles we had already come. The only sign of habitation was an ancient looking building two or three hundred yards away and a couple of battered and mucky buses. Our engine and the long train it pulled sat like a beached whale as passengers continued to step down. A few locals, though locals from exactly where was hard to fathom, ran forward and tried to sell pieces of fish, a cucumber, or maybe some berries to the alighting travellers. Betty and I waited in the snow beside our cases and watched it all while Irina and Angelique held a lengthy discussion in their native tongue. Finally they pointed to one of the ramshackle buses.

Russia is vast. You can't just jump on a train to any town which takes your fancy. This was as close as the train got to Veliki Ustiug. We would travel the next hundred miles or so by bus. And we were lucky. For most of the chug-a-chug journey we had a seat. Which reminds me of another earlier faux pas I made during one of my first bus journeys in Cherepovets, before I had honed my understanding of the Russian language. This time, while standing in front of a well dressed middle-aged citizen in the packed bus the citizen suddenly addressed me in Russian. Unprepared and not expecting conversation, I got it all wrong. I thought the citizen asked me if I understood Russian. One word leapt to my mouth – "*nyet*" – meaning "no". The middle-aged citizen gave me a look which would have soured Russian yoghurt and contemptuously pushed me out of the way and got off the bus at the next stop. When I had time to reflect I realized the citizen had actually asked me, in the nicest possible way, if I would be so kind as to excuse him as he wanted to get off the bus. I don't think "*nyet*" was the answer he was looking for.

At the bus depot on the outskirts of our destination, Veliki Ustiug, we were met by a Zhiguli saloon driven by a young man named Sasha – another fine piece of Angelique organisation – and treated to an hour's drive of the ancient and historic town which straddled a mile-wide river frozen solid for the duration of the winter. The battered and rusty Zhiguli coped easily with the snow and ice as we skidded and slid around the town. Veliki Ustiug's architecture certainly reflected the antiquity of the town. It's a country town and like all Russian settlements there is no want of space. Streets are wide and buildings set well apart, a throw-back to when all Russian homes were made from wood and the risk of fire was great. The farther apart, the safer the buildings. If one did go up in a blaze as the result of a kicked over oil lamp or an unattended open fire it would hopefully burn on its own and not bring half the village down with it. Many of the structures and houses of Veliki Ustiug are still made from wood. We would dwell in one for the next three days. From inside the Zhiguli I observed the citizens of Veliki Ustiug, well wrapped up against the freezing cold of maybe fifteen or twenty below, wander stoically about the streets as traffic slithered and careered all over the place with little respect for the rules of the road, or even the footpath, but without ever causing a mishap. Sasha drove us all over town and on to the outskirts on the far side. All the houses here were of wooden construction – not lathes of wood hammered on to a frame – but solid buildings made from whole pine logs, and not two buildings the same for each was hand built by its owner, or previous owner. Because of the depth of snow I couldn't be quite sure, but I thought there was some suggestion of a layout of streets and avenues. But they certainly weren't the boring "seen one you've seen 'em all" developments we know at home It seems that in Veliki Ustuig you simply found a piece of land, chopped down a few trees and built your house, pretty much as and where you wanted it. I don't know if plans or planning permission ever entered into the equation. I doubt that they did. Sasha drove us erratically along a deeply snow-banked lane and up to one wooden home. I could see, and almost feel, the strength of it, solid, with real character. Sasha pulled in and switched off the engine. We had evidently arrived. Where, or for what purpose, I had no idea. I gazed through the car window as an elderly man, upright, and with a strong noble face shuffled down the path from the house toward us. I took in his workaday clothes and grey hair peeking from under his fur hat and I liked the man before I knew who he was or anything about him. He greeted us with a big smile as we struggled out from the car. Angelique introduced us to Feydor, and then to his wife Lola. Lola was a small bright lady with an equally ready smile. Angelique explained Feydor and Lola were to be our hosts for the few days we would stay in Veliki Ustuig. Without a word of English, but with much Russian and many hugs, Feydor and Lola threw their arms around us and bade us a warm welcome to their home.

Fedyor had built his house with his own hands when Lola and he were married, just after the war. It wasn't the sort of home you'd find in the glossy magazines; far superior. Practical, homely, built for comfort and durability, not for show, and to last many lifetimes, it was the sort of house a man would be proud to call "home". Feydor and Lola led the way up the snow-covered path to their front door. The first thing we did was remove our footwear as soon as we stepped into the hallway. We learn fast. Fedyor eyed my boots. He picked them up and examined them closely, turning them over and over, checking the soles and the uppers. He smiled, then nodded his head. That's when I realised I owned a good pair of boots. We removed our damp overcoats and scarves and hats and tossed them over the stove. A Russian stove is a brick built affair, very often faced with high quality decorative tiles. It is usually about seven or eight feet high, ten feet long and four or five feet wide. It provides heat for the entire house. A set of steps or a ladder gives access to the top where it is possible to lie down and sleep and keep warm in the harsh Russian winter. Fedyor didn't sleep on top of the stove. At least not during our stay. But we often saw him climb up there and sit enjoying a cigarette, his feet dangling over the side. The Russian stove is totally enclosed except for a small iron door through which blocks of wood are fed. Every dwelling has a stack of blocks, hewn by its owner, built neatly outside the home, enough to last the winter. Preparation is always the thing in Russia. You just don't turn up the central heating or ask the coalman to deliver another bag of fuel, though Feydor's home was fitted with electricity. The other door in Feydor and Lola's stove gave access to a large oven. One day we watched Lola shred fresh cabbage on a little wooden table. She kneaded and rolled out a big lump of dough and set about making cabbage pies, each one about the size of a Cornish pastie. When Lola had packed cabbage and cheese firmly into the prepared pieces of dough Fedyor held out a long-shafted implement similar to a garden spade. Lola set half a dozen pies on the spade end. Feydor swung open the hot oven door and inserted the spade into the depths of the glowing oven. With a gentle twist of his wrist he slid the pies off the spade to bake and withdrew the long shaft back before slamming the door shut. In five minutes the pies were ready and Feydor was called upon again, this time to reverse the process. Betty and I enjoyed Lola's baking. The pies were delicious, and produced by a technology several hundred years old. I considered again the consumer society and must-have products back home. Feydor and Lola didn't need them. They lived as their parents and grandparents before would have lived. And Feydor told me that, though well into his seventies, he grows and harvests his own vegetables and fruits which he and Lola store and carefully preserve to last throughout the hard winter. There isn't any supermarket.

Our hosts prepared for us a small feast for that first meal – the pies made from cabbage, cheese and fish, cucumbers, beef, fresh cranberry juice, olives, black and white breads, sweetmeats, caviar, coffee and *chi*. And vodka. Always, always, the vodka. I tried my best to defend myself from Feydor and his bottle – or to be more accurate, bottles of vodka. But he would have none of it, filling and refilling my glass over and over again. As I saw him coming at me with the vodka once again I covered my glass with my hand in polite Western style and declared "*Nyet! Nyet spaseeba bolshoi!*" – only to be caught out when I turned my head in conversation with Lola, giving Feydor the opportunity to sneak up behind me and fill the glass again. Good manners dictated the vodka had to be disposed off. Down my throat. I'll always remember the great kindness and hospitality Feydor and Lola bestowed upon us.

After our meal I felt a little thirsty – for water! In Lola's kitchen

I'd noticed a brass tap set into the wall. Strangely, there wasn't any sink beneath the tap. Just a white enamel bucket half full of water sitting on the floor directly under it. I pointed to the tap, indicating to Feydor I would like a drink. I expected him to turn on the tap and fill a mug with water. Instead, he walked to the other end of the kitchen and flicked on what I thought was an electric light switch. I looked on in astonishment as water poured forth from the tap straight into the bucket. That was clever. I'd never seen that done before. It transpired the water came up directly from Fedyor's own well sunk deep in the earth. It was pumped up by electricity. Pure, cold, clear water, the best I'd ever tasted. I drunk my fill from the metal ladle in the bucket, just as the cowboys did in the old western movies.

After I'd slaked my thirst Feydor motioned me to put on my boots and coat and hat. "*Banya*!" he exclaimed excitedly. "*Banya*! *Banya*!." Feydor rubbed his tummy as if satisfied with a good meal. He raised his hand to his mouth and threw his head back as if downing a vodka, and finally rubbed both hands all over his body as though he were washing himself. I had no idea what he was trying to communicate to me.

I appealed to Angelique and Irina. "What is it? What does Feydor mean?"

"You will see!," laughed Irina. "Go outside. Fedyor will show you!

Fedyor led the way through the snow and down toward the bottom of his back garden. The sky was clear and starry and I could almost hear the silence as we trudged through the snow which was piled shoulder high on either side of us. At the bottom of the garden stood what I assumed to be an ordinary garden shed, snow covered and seemingly lit by an oil-lamp. Garden shed it was not. Fedyor opened the door and ushered me into a wave of boiling steaming heat which immediately took my breath away. Half the shed was filled by a huge metal stove on top of which sat an open iron tank brimming with scalding hot water. Two or three little wooden forms, obviously to be used as seats, skirted the walls. A couple of basins sat on the forms. One basin was filled with a greenish water and an armful of long grasses. A few rough scrubbing brushes, which I reckoned could inflict varying degrees of pain and torture if applied to the human body, hung from the walls. Fedyor grinned broadly. He pointed at me. "*Banya*!" he exclaimed gleefully. "*Banya*! *Banya*!" Feydor laughed loudly and repeated the previous washing movement with his hands all over his body. He pointed to me again. "*Banya*!" I nodded, not very much the wiser. I finally coaxed Feydor, very much against his will, to let me return to the house to consult with Angelique and Irina.

Angelique and Irina explained as Feydor and Lola looked on, nodding enthusiastically though they didn't understand a word of the English. "In Russia, Hugh," said Irina, "it is great luxury to have *banya*, which is what Feydor is showing you, and has prepared especially for you. Like Turkish bath. You go to *banya*. Take off all clothes. Sit down. Stay for two hours. There is much heat. Soon all your pores will open. Sweat and impurities will leave your body. Fill basin with water, as hot as you can. Wash body and use brushes to clean skin. Do five or six times. Each time make water a little colder. At finish, wash body only with green water of special river grasses. Then, when all is done, go outside. No clothes. Roll in snow. Very good for health." I nodded, wondering if Feydor had ever heard of a bathtub and a bottle of Raydox. But when I came on this trip to Russia I wanted above all to live exactly as the Russian people lived, whatever way that might be. Much to Feydor's delight, I consented to take my *banya*. That was a most unusual and exhilarating experience, with Feydor dropping by every fifteen or twenty minutes to ensure I was enjoying the utmost pleasures his *banya* afforded me. I don't normally sweat. But that night, in the steaming hot *banya*, with the glass at about twenty below outside and going through the roof inside, sweat poured in rivers from every part of my body. I was cleansed as I'd never been cleansed before.

Feydor laughed joyfully and congratulated me and clapped my

back and poured a stiff vodka down my throat when I returned from the *banya*, though he was slightly disappointed to learn I had not taken the roll in the snow. But now it was the turn of Betty and Angelique and Irina. They went for the works – snow et all – together. I think I've got a photograph somewhere …

It was nearly midnight when we retired after more feasting and much drinking of healths. Maybe the average Russian doesn't expect to encounter too many sleep-over guests. There certainly never seems to be an over abundance of spare bedrooms. Or beds. Once again we would sleep on a sofa-bed in the living room. A gentle thick snow drifted quietly outside our window as we prepared for slumber. But each time Betty and I attempted to remove an article of clothing Feydor charged into the room triumphantly waving the vodka bottle, perhaps another tray of food, or maybe to see if we desired to have the television turned on. Feydor was so pleased and excited at having foreign guests under his roof he couldn't bear to be parted from us, even at bed-time. The situation wasn't too bad for me. It was even funny. But Betty was like the proverbial fan-dancer, just about, but afraid to remove another article of clothing in case Feydor made another sudden entrance. She finally managed to get a nightdress pulled on and leap into bed – just before Feydor made his final entrance, waving a chamber pot for our convenience. I can't remember if he left it under the bed or not. I was asleep, all at ease and comfortable in the stillness and quietness of the old Russian home on a very snowy night.

That night Veliki Ustiug saw its heaviest snowfall in ten years. But in the morning Angelique insisted on taking us in Sasha's Zhiguli for another and more comprehensive tour of the town and its environs. Angelique also said she would like to visit the grave of her grandmother Maria who had lived in Veliki Ustiug. We drove to the cemetery, away beyond the suburbs and out to a country area. The cemetery wasn't what I had expected. It wasn't a wide open area with graves laid out in straight lines. Arm in arm with Angelique and Irina we walked through the knee-deep snow into a little forest The pine and birch trees were tall and aged and laden with the overnight snow. The graves were laid out in an irregular fashion, just where space would permit between the trees. Each grave had a headstone or some simple marker which always held a photograph of the departed soul. I was struck by the large number of photographs which depicted beautiful young ladies, handsome men, teenagers, children and babies and all looking exceedingly healthy and full of life. I asked Angelique why so many of the photographs displayed the departed in their younger years. I was taken aback when Angelique informed me the photographs were usually those which had been taken nearest to the time when the deceased had passed on. I failed to establish why so many had died at such a relatively young age.

Respectfully, we stood back as Angelique approached a grave which we could see had special significance for her. The grave, like the others, had at one end a sort of metal circular table about a foot in diameter and supported on a pole about three feet above the grave. I looked on in silence as Angelique slowly brushed away the snow from the top of the table. She opened a plastic carrier bag and picked out a few sweets she had purchased earlier in the town. Angelique laid five or six of the sweets carefully on top of the table. She opened the bag again and brought out a few pieces of bread and cake. Very carefully, she placed them beside the sweets. Angelique turned to us. She handed us some sweets and bread and with tear-rimmed eyes motioned us to place them beside those she had already laid on the little table. We did so, gently, quietly, without understanding. It was a moving experience. Tears trickled from my eyes. I tasted their salt on my lips. Then we moved back and watched as Angelique stood with bowed head. Reverently, she made the sign of the cross, wiped her eyes, and moved slowly away from the grave at the foot of the tall trees.

We all clasped hands. Then, at a suitable moment, when Angelique smiled again and we all moved away from the grave, I asked her the meaning of the bread and sweets. "The sweets were my grandmother's favourite," Angelique murmured softly. "I leave them for her. Also bread. Tradition says it is for spirit of the departed. But little birds will come and eat the bread. Poor people will also come and eat the bread. And sweets. It is good." It was. And touchingly beautiful.

As we wandered through the trees toward the cemetery exit we met a very old woman. She was obviously poor. I stopped and spoke to her in her native language. She knew immediately we were foreigners and expressed surprise we should speak with her. Tears rolled from her eyes as she greeted me with many Russian words which I couldn't understand. I put my arms around the dear lady and hugged her as she planted kiss after kiss on my cheeks. I asked Irina to ask the old lady her name and why she was alone in the cemetery so early on this snowy morning. The old lady informed us her name was Maria, by coincidence the same as Angelique's grandmother whose grave we had just visited. She told us she rose at three o'clock every morning to pray for all the saints in all Russia, and then for Christians all over the world. Who was I, she wanted to know? Where did I come from? I told her I was a writer, from Northern Ireland, and when I returned home to my own country I would tell many people about her, and maybe, if she would let me take her photograph, I would have it published in a newspaper. This caused Maria to weep even more profusely. As I took the photograph, I too shed tears. I will always remember Maria. The world needs more Marias.

We drove back to the town and the frozen river. In the crisp morning air we walked out on the ice for about a quarter of a mile, viewing the snow-clad town and its churches and cupolas from different angles. Then we piled into the Zhiguli again and set off on another mystery tour. Sasha drove us into town and pulled up outside the local radio-station. Another of Angelique's surprises, this one especially for me. "Hugh," exclaimed Angelique. "Veliki Ustiug radio station want to interview you. What you think about Russia. And Veliki Ustiug. You will speak?" Back home I'd done about forty broadcasts on BBC

Radio with Walter Love, utilising all the professional facilities the BBC could offer. I never imagined I'd one day be broadcasting from a Russian radio studio. The station was small – very small – and run by a handful of enthusiastic volunteers. I would be interviewed by Leonid Suranov, Chief Director of Veliki Ustiug Radio. Irina would interpret. The station's equipment wasn't much beyond what the average hi-fi enthusiast in the West might enjoy in his lounge. The editor of the local newspaper – not wishing to miss a story – was also in attendance. After much discussion about Russia and Northern Ireland and writers and writing, the interview took an unexpected turn when I was suddenly asked if I believed in God. This was one question I had not expected to be asked on Russian radio. It took me aback. I replied in the affirmative and gave the reasons for my belief. The questioning about Christianity became more and more intense until I finally asked the interviewer the reason for his interest in this subject.

"We interview before some people from the West," replied Leonid, now in the role of interviewee. "You are first who say you believe in God. All others say don't believe. Are atheists. You surprise us. This is why we are interested."

I promised Leonid when I returned home I would write about his radio station and broadcast about it on BBC Radio. That pleased him very much. And I kept my promise. The tapes of the BBC broadcast are now in the library of Veliki Ustiug Radio. Later that evening Angelique, the lady of a thousand surprises, visited us with another. We were to get ready to attend another birthday party to be thrown in my honour at the home of one of Angelique's relatives across town. I don't know where Sasha and the Zhiguli was on this occasion, but we travelled over by bus. The house was similar in style, but maybe larger than Feydor's. It was one of many wooden homes set in a bank of snow in no particular order. As we entered the large homely house and removed our footwear we could see the long table which filled the room and sagged with piles of Russian food and drink. I looked at Betty. We knew what was coming! It was going to be a long night, in which East-West relations would be strengthened even further. One by one we were introduced to the twenty-five or so members of the family and friends who had gathered in for the party. Russians don't need a second bidding to a knees-up. Again there was much toasting of our health and our homeland. Then the eating and drinking began in earnest. Everything and everybody was toasted. Myself, Betty, our children, grand-children, great-grandchild who was on the way, the food, winter, the coming spring, the vodka itself and anything else which came to mind. Then, gifts to me, from everyone, each handed over with a formal handshake and a kiss – even from the men – and a hug fit to take my breath away. Those were the preliminaries. Then everyone was on the floor singing and dancing to the accordion player in typically Russian fashion. Many of the humorous songs sung that night had been written especially for me by our hosts and performed specially in my honour. Although I couldn't quite grasp the lyrics, our hosts certainly did, and fell about laughing. Most of the musical turns were performed by the much talented Nina and her friends who did costume changes between each number. Nina was a tall grey-haired good-looking lady who'd lived through Russia's titanic struggle in the Second World War. Where she got the energy to dance and sing at full fling for half the night was beyond me. But Nina and her co-performers were superb in their song and dance routines – streets ahead of so–called "stars" I've seen on our television screen at home. What a night! What dear, dear friends! What music! What laughter! But finally it was time to take our leave and crunch again through the fairy-tale avenues of wooden houses with yellow lights gleaming in every snow-covered window, toward the bus, and toward Feydor and Lola's dear little home. Once there we tumbled straight into bed. We were fast asleep before Feydor had time to dig out the vodka bottle. Or the chamber pot.

Next morning just after breakfast, Lola suddenly became quite excited about something she'd just glimpsed through the window.

I looked out. In the narrow lane, squeezing between the banks of snow, a large black saloon about the size and age of a ten year old Ford Granada had pulled up outside. I could see from the excitement on Lola's face it wouldn't have been everyday such a vehicle would have been seen in her avenue.

"It's for you, Hugh and Betty," laughed Angelique. "Mayor of Veliki Ustiug sends his greetings and limousine to take you to Father Frost's Winter Palace! About ten kilometres. We go!"

I'd always known, ever since I was a little boy, there was a real Santa Claus. And that there must be some secret place where he lived, though I didn't know where it might be. I'd never doubted it. Now I can say, without fear of contradiction, I have not only visited the Winter Palace where the real Santa Claus lives – I have personally met the gentleman. Father Frost's huge wooden palace, set smack in the middle of the snowy forest, is majestic and a delight to behold. In room after room and on staircase after staircase beautiful snow-maidens danced and sang and performed all the delights of Christmas time in the gloriously decorated palace. Christmas trees filled the rooms and lined the staircases, each one weighed down with gloriously wrapped boxes and sparkling fairy-lights and toys. In every room a storyteller weaved the magical tales of Christmas and folk-stories of the season and of the mysterious peoples who dwell in the depths of the forest. I couldn't catch all the words. But as a yarn spinner myself I knew these storytellers had their audiences hanging with baited breath on every word as they spun their magic. They were good. The palace was resplendent and fit for only one person – the real Santa Claus.

As the snow maidens in their tunics of scarlet and white danced and sang in the great room on the ground floor Father Frost – the real Santa Claus – suddenly made a dramatic entrance on the huge balcony above us. I knew immediately he was the real Santa Claus – magnificent, noble, and easily seven foot in height with a rich blood-red cloak trimmed with white fur trailing yards behind him as he slowly and royally descended the staircase to the gasps and applause of his audience. Father Frost moved regally over to his large gold throne and sat down like a king. In a deep rich voice he welcomed everyone to his palace and especially welcomed Hugh and Betty from Northern Ireland. More proof of Angelique's pull with people in high places! Father Frost presented us with gifts from his palace and consented to have his photograph taken with us. I've still got that photograph. I'm glad I have. It isn't everyone who gets to meet the real Santa Claus. If I didn't have the photograph – who would believe I'd met the man himself? When we finally took our leave of Father Frost and the delightful Winter Palace we were greeted outside the huge wooden gates by another television crew begging us for an interview. It was my privilege to answer the questions and express again our pleasure at being able to visit Father Frost and the beautiful Veliki Ustuig.

Next morning, after breakfast with Feydor and Lola, another surprise. Again Lola flapped about excitedly. She pointed through the window. So did Angelique and Feydor and Irina. "Look Hugh! Look out window!" shouted Angelique. I did. I couldn't believe my eyes. A huge *troika*, pulled by a strong and noble-shouldered grey horse stood at the end of Feydor's path. I'd always wanted to ride a Russian *troika*. But Angelique had told me in her letters *troikas* were now a rarity in Russia. Now there was one in the avenue outside!

"Where's my camera!" I shouted excitedly. "Where's my camera!" This might be the only opportunity I'd get to photograph a real Russian *troika*. I had to photograph it before it disappeared up the avenue. I couldn't understand why Angelique urged me to get my boots and coat and hat and not worry just yet about the camera.

"Come Hugh!" laughed Angelique. "It's for you! *Troika* ride for you!"

I couldn't believe it! For me! A Russian *troika*-ride – something I'd only dreamed about! Dear Angelique! We piled into our warm clothes and bundled down the path and scrambled aboard the *troika*, Betty, Angelique, Irina, the driver and myself. The *troika* wasn't a delicate thing. Nor was the horse which pulled it. I could see and feel the strength in those broad haunches as we fairly clattered and slithered and bounced away through the lanes and into the streets of Veliki Ustiug. The bell on the horse's harness tinkled sweetly as we sped along at easily twenty miles an hour. We held on tightly as the *troika* bounced and swayed and threw us all over the place, much to the amusement and delight of the local citizens. Dreams can come true. I know.

We shopped and dined in Veliki Ustuig and finally wended our way back in the early evening to Feydor and Lola's cosy home. After another supper and not a little vodka – it had got to the stage where I could handle it okay – Lola demonstrated her skills with knife and birch bark on the kitchen table. Anything can be made from the birch-bark – from a bunch of roses to a finely detailed bookmark. Lola has created many works of art from the bark of the birch-tree. Examples of her fine skills can be seen in museums and galleries and even a few palaces across Russia. We'd seen some of them. We looked on as Lola prepared her work station – the tiny kitchen table – and her tools – a single sharp bladed knife almost small enough to fit into the palm of her hand, and a small reading light to help her ailing sight. Lola took a piece of the bark, about eight inches square, and peeled the back from it until the material was the thickness of a piece of thin cardboard. She would make a bookmark. And she did. Lola didn't use templates or straight-edges or draw a design. She went straight in, cutting with the blade, twisting and turning, piercing and marking, and within the space of five minutes produced an intricately worked design and product which looked as though it had been produced by a computer on an assembly line. But Lola used only eyes and fingers to create fine beauty from her bark. She made it look so easy I thought I could do it. Lola smiled and bade me sit down in her seat. She handed me the knife and piece of bark. I couldn't even make a clean cut let alone any semblance of design.

Parting is always a time of sorrow. Next morning we left our dear friends Feydor and Lola to make the journey back to Cherepovets. That was heart-rending. How is it possible the human heart can attach itself to and come to love dearly those it has known for less than a handful of days? I tried to explain it within my own being as we struggled to say dasveedanya to two dear people who had taken us into their home and into their hearts. We expressed as best we could to Feydor and Lola the happiness we'd known with them in their home. Feydor hugged us. Tears filled his eyes as he made a long emotional speech, not a word of which I could understand. Irina translated. "Fedyor says his soul and Lola's soul is at one with Hugh and Betty. When you entered their home they knew immediately your heart was with them. You have not been their guests – you have been their family. You are one with them. It saddens their heart you must leave. Come back again." We were humbled by these gracious sentiments, uttered by a simple Russian countryman whom but for chance I might never have known, but whom I would never, ever forget. Feydor hauled out his sledge from a hut beside the *banya* and piled our suitcases on to it. Then the six of us set off through the lanes toward the bus-stop. Feydor proudly hauled the sledge, which he'd made himself, with Lola beside him. The sledge slid easily along in the fresh snow as we tramped toward the bus which would take us to Yahidra and the train for Cherepovets. I was pleased when Feydor invited me to take a turn at pulling the sledge. It required little or no effort. And it was fuel free and environmentally friendly. Everything was fine as we waited and chatted cheerily at the bus-stop as a light snow began to fall. I looked up as the bus turned into our street. It chugged noisily along the snowy road and pulled in beside us. It was time to say goodbye – perhaps for ever – to Feydor and Lola. That's when, emotionally, I went to pieces. I struggled to control myself as we hugged and kissed the old couple. Why was I getting so emotionally upset over two old people I'd only met two or three days ago, and would probably never see again? We boarded the bus. The four of us struggled into our seats and waved goodbye to Feydor and Lola. But the bus didn't move. That gave Feydor time to get up to his old tricks. Not wishing us to depart, he jumped on to the bus. He strode up the aisle, right up to my seat. He threw his arms around me and hugged me tightly and kissed me on both cheeks, chattering away in a fast Russian, and repeatedly laying the palm of his hand on his heart. That was too much for me. Tears flowed unchecked from my eyes and I sunk my head in my chest so no one would see. But Irina and Angelique and other passengers did see, and knew what was going on in my heart. Finally Feydor was coaxed to leave the bus. He stood on the street with Lola, smiling and waving, and laying his hand on his heart. The bus began to move. I turned my head and waved to Feydor and Lola as they stood beside the sledge. We blew kisses, through the window, into the swirling snow, and into their heart. This time, it really was dasveedanya. We were on our way back to Yahidra and Cherepovets.

The hundred miles or so bus drive to Yahidra was accomplished in darkness. It wasn't a journey for those of nervous disposition. We skidded and slid about at great speeds on the snow and ice covered road with a few incidents *en route* which would be front page news at home but which were simply par for the course in Russia. A couple of times we managed to get stuck half way up a snow covered hill on which the bus tyres couldn't get any sort of grip. I thought we weren't going to make it. The engine of the bus roared and revved as the tyres spun hopelessly and the bus actually began to slither back down the hill. It careered the whole way back down. Whether that was by design of the driver, or by default, I did not know. Nobody showed the slightest alarm, except perhaps Betty and myself. The bus sat motionless at the bottom of the hill, engine still revving. The driver pulled out a cigarette, lit it and took a long drag. He surveyed the ascent ahead and continued to smoke. The passengers offered him all sorts of advice on how to surmount the problem and although I couldn't understand all that was going on I knew he was digesting the advice and debating with them the best way to get over the hill. Eventually he took a severely long suck on the cigarette. He rammed the bus into gear. He gave the engine full revs, let in the clutch and roared up the hill in a cacophony of noise and burning clutch and blue smoke.

Yahidra railway station is a small basic structure probably built in Tolstoy's time, and as far as I could make out, un-changed since then. A few wooden seats fringed an uncomfortable waiting room, which was just that. It was simple in the extreme with nothing in the way of decoration apart from the green distemper paint on the walls. Just as in Tolstoy's time, I thought, as I remembered my literary hero had spent his last day on earth in just such a place. But I was pleased I was, even in this modern age, experiencing another piece of old Russia.

The train to Cherepovets wasn't due for another hour. We hung about the draughty waiting-room, literally kicking our toes. Fifteen minutes before the train was due Angelique rose to her feet. She grabbed her luggage and signalled to us.

"We go. Get train."

I hadn't seen any sign of the train or heard any announcement that it was about to arrive. But I had learned enough about Russia, and had enough confidence in Angelique's judgement in matters of every sort to know if she said "go!" the sensible thing to do was go!

Betty and I struggled with our bags of heavy luggage. We were taking back twice as much as we'd arrived with. We trudged behind Irina and Angelique out to the dimly lit platform in front of the station. I expected Angelique to stop and wait for the train. She didn't. She pointed down the line, away beyond the station, into the darkness of the barren snow-covered landscape. "We go!" she exclaimed.

I had no idea why we were tramping away from the lights of the station into the bitterly cold wind which drove the snow hard into our face. The snow was deep, right up to our knees, and our heavy luggage made any progress along the track difficult. As we floundered about and tried to keep up with Angelique I began to laugh at the absurdity of it all. Where were we going? This was no way to catch a train. Why didn't we just stand at the platform and wait for it?

"Not laugh, Hugh!", Angelique admonished me as she turned round. "Not funny! Come. *Bistrah*!, Quickly!"

We ploughed through the snow for another two or three hundred yards until Angelique finally called a halt. "We wait here." "Here" was in the darkness of the night at the edge of the track with the freezing cold chattering our teeth despite our layers of clothes and the railway station practically out of sight. "Train come soon," Angelique advised us. "Then we go. Quickly!"

We nodded and wearily laid down our bags and cases. I don't think Betty felt the same about it as I did. This was tough work, uncomfortable even, and strange. But for me it was an experience to stand in the middle of nowhere on a dark snowy Russian night. Waiting. For a train. The wind was bitter and stabbed us repeatedly through our layers of heavy clothing. To keep ourselves warm we threw snowballs and chased each other up and down the track. Then in the distance I glimpsed the dull yellow light of the train and heard its mournful cry as it journeyed toward us. It seemed to take forever to arrive. When it did it swept past at a great speed, whipping up the snow and hurling it into our faces. The carriages went on and on for ever and I thought they would never end. Now I realised why Angelique had dragged us away out here instead of waiting in the comparative warmth of the station waiting-room. "Go! Go! Go!," she shouted, shoving Betty in front of her and plunging through the deep snow even farther along the line away from the station toward the seemingly endless line of carriages which towered and roared past us.

I'd seen this on Russian television. Citizens plunging through deep snow to catch a train. Stumbling. Falling down. Getting to their feet, plunging on again, falling once more until they finally reached their carriage. I could never understand why they didn't wait at the station. Now I did. The train was extremely long.

Angelique had told us it only stopped at the station for three minutes. If you weren't on board, in the correct carriage when the train pulled out, too bad.

"*Bistrah*! *Bistrah*!" encouraged Angelique as we scrambled along, hardly able to draw a breath in the freezing cold. A lady just in front of me fell face first into the snow. I made a grab at her as I stumbled past, just about managing to haul her to her feet. Then I crashed down myself, bags and cases on top of me. When I staggered to my feet and spat out a mouthful of snow I saw Betty. She was on her knees, sobbing. The effort was proving too much for her. With help from Angelique and Irina we grabbed her and trailed her along to our carriage.

You don't just step on to a Russian train. Especially if you're in the middle of the countryside. You climb up, a height of about three or four feet. It was a real battle to get Betty into the carriage with all her luggage. I was all in myself. When we finally collapsed on to our seats I fought to get my breath back. When I did I just sat there and laughed, and laughed, probably with relief and the thrill of the experience. Betty didn't laugh. It had been a tough and very difficult experience for her. She sobbed. Hard. There was no doubt she was distressed. But we finally got her calmed down and cheered up with a vodka coffee and a few Russian jokes.

We finally arrived home for our last night in Galena's little flat. One more night, then one more afternoon for a final stroll around our adopted town of Cherepovets. On the last evening Sergi arrived in his reliable Zhiguli to drive us to the railway station with Angelique and Galena. Angelique would travel the overnight train journey with us to Moscow, to see us safely on our plane.

All our dear Cherepovets friends were waiting for us at the station, right on the line, as we came forward to board the train. Sergi, wife Irina and daughter Anya, and many of those we had met at my birthday party. Irina, our translator and good friend and travelling companion was there with husband Yura and children Anton and Anastasia – all assembled, wrapped up against the cold, pressing more and more gifts upon us as we prepared to say goodbye. So many hugs. So many kisses. So many invitations to return. Return? We didn't want to leave. A last kiss. A final hug. A tearful parting, then more blowing of kisses through the lighted carriage window and waving and waving until our dear friends disappeared from our sight, but not from our heart, as the train pulled away. Beautiful, kind, warm-hearted Russian friends. They had shared their homes, their food, their culture, their joys and laughter and music and hearts with us. The only thing they asked of us was that when we returned home we would tell everyone in the west that they 'were not bad people.'

In the morning we awoke as the train nosed in to the outskirts of Moscow. "Look Hugh!," exclaimed Angelique as she pointed through the window. "It is the first day of Spring." Angelique was right. In Russia, spring arrives in a day. And stays. The Moscow river, frozen solid through the long winter, was melting, the waters edging and flowing along the dripping snow banks. The sky was blue, the sun shone. As Galena would say, it was a nice day. The last of the snows slid from the birch trees. Winter was ended. And so were our travels through Russia. We had seen the best of the Russian winter, in all its might and stately grandeur and iron grip. Now, in a single morning, we'd experienced the glory of the Russian spring when the whole country came to life once more. We spent our final few hours wandering round some of the beautiful Moscow parks with Angelique and her friend Anatoly who'd met us at the railway station. We strolled with the tourists and young lovers, with old people, and young children. Then, finally, there came the fondest, and most poignant of farewells to dear Angelique at Sheremetevo airport. Our return to beautiful Russia, and its lovely people, was over. Dasveedanya, dear friends. Until we return. Again.

Frankie Laine – My Friend

Winter nights were long and dark and often dreary in our little Ballyhay cottage. Especially for a youngster like me. A few years after the war, in the early 1950's, electricity still hadn't reached the countryside. We had lamplight – and happily for me, an ancient Marconi battery wireless. Sometimes the wireless worked. Sometimes it didn't. But the wireless opened up a whole new world to me – the world of show-business and the great singing stars of the generation. Of course they were far away, unreachable, untouchable stars. But what pleasure they brought to me each night as I tuned – if the battery was charged – to enjoy Vera Lynn, Donald Peers, Gracie Fields, and the great American entertainers Bing Crosby, Guy Mitchell, Jo Stafford, Kay Starr and Frankie Laine.

Frankie Laine was the favourite of all my favourites. I was totally enraptured as I listened to the warm sensitive voice delivering *I Believe*, on the wireless, a recording Laine kept in the U.K. music charts for a staggering nine months, eighteen weeks of which were right at the top in the Number One position. As I grew older, right through my teenage years and the entire 1950's Frankie Laine dominated the musical world with a procession of hit recordings. Who doesn't recall the pulsating *High Noon, Answer Me, Granada, Cool Water, Moonlight Gambler* and *Woman in Love*, to mention only a few. Everyone remembers "roll 'em up - head 'em out" – the theme from the long-running *Rawhide* TV series. And Laine's was the strong dramatic voice behind a host of highly acclaimed westerns films, including *Blazing Saddles.*

I never imagined a youngster like me, living in the sticks, would ever see my hero of the show-business world perform on stage. But across the years I have learned if your dreams are neither mercenary nor mean, and you hold on to them long enough, there is an unexplainable something which creates tiny circumstances, slowly, over a long period of time and blends them together until finally they bring about the fulfilment of the most unattainable of dreams. In childhood I had many dreams. To discover a town full of books. To be a writer. A broadcaster. To travel to the great secret land of Russia. To live with a Russian family. To see Frankie Laine on stage. Just once … All, all these, and much more, have come to pass. I cannot explain any of it. But as I reflect back through the years, and on all the seemingly insignificant incidents which brought about the realization of my dreams, one thing is obvious. Nowhere along the way did I force the issue or deliberately and ruthlessly pursue a course to make the events happen. But happen they did.

I was thirty one years old before I saw Frankie Laine on stage. I didn't know it then, but that was simply the beginning of a warm friendship which has continued for thirty years, during which my wife Betty and I have often been honoured guests in Frank's lovely San Diego home. But Frankie Laine, a colossus in the popular music business, is much more than just a maker of hit records. Country, blues, standards, gospel, popular and jazz are all equally part of Laine's vast repertoire with which he has delighted fans all over the world from the 1940's to the present day.

Jazz was, and still is, his first love. It was in this field he 'scuffed around' in the music business in the early days before making his breakthrough with his first hit, *That's My Desire*, on Mercury records. Hit followed hit after that. But it was only the beginning. Mitch Miller, Frank's producer, moved over to Columbia records, taking Frank (as he prefers to be known to his friends) with him and re-directing his career into the popular music domain where he would achieve worldwide success.

Such was Laine's impact across the Atlantic on U.K. audiences he had chart hits right through the 1950s and on into the 1960s. His albums remain top sellers today. Recently the singer returned to the music of his roots and released a marvellous new CD, *Old Man Jazz*. And of course every jazz fan will recall the superb *Jazz Spectacular* produced when Laine teamed up with the legendary Buck Clayton to cut the album which is still held in the highest esteem in the jazz field today. Clayton declared the album to be one which "will take a long time to equal, a perfect example of jazz singing coupled with jazz instrumental solos."

With a string of smash-hit movies, TV and radio shows, a starring role in a *Rawhide* episode, stage performances to packed houses, including the memorable 1954 Royal Command Performance at the London Palladium, Frank has also recorded with Doris Day, Johnny Ray, Jimmy Boyd, The Four Lads and the great Jo Stafford. Co-authoring his autobiography *That Lucky Old Son*, Laine has done just about everything, and is still doing more.

Frankie Laine's career, which isn't over yet, spans an incredible seven decades. It's unlikely any other singer has had the appeal and staying power to be working and finding an audience over that vast range of time in the fickle world of show-business. Perhaps Laine's continued popularity can be traced to two simple facts. Frankie Laine is a true musical talent – an entertainer who always delivers, on stage, on screen, or in the recording studio, a quality performance. But Frank is not only a superb entertainer – he is widely regarded by his fans and fellow artistes as the nicest man in show business. Knowing Frank for all these years, I understand why. But I am not alone in calling Frankie Laine a true gentleman, and one of the nicest people I have ever met, my friend. A host of others can say the same. What other top-flight entertainer would answer every letter he receives, gives his fans his home telephone number, call them himself from time to time, and invite them up to his beautiful hill-top home overlooking the bay in lovely San Diego's Point Loma when they're in town. He has lived his life, in and out of show-business, with the highest respect and regard for others, totally unaffected by his success and untainted by scandal of any sort. His more than forty year marriage to actress Nan Grey only ended when Nan collapsed in Frank's arms and passed away in 1993 leaving him devastated. But family and friends and fans supported Frank in his time of sorrow. It was the same people, almost eight hundred of them, who travelled from all over the world to help Frank celebrate his 90th birthday in the plush old world U.S. Grant Hotel, close to San Diego's historic Gaslamp Quarter. Betty and I were privileged to be among them.

I'd been at Frank's 85th birthday party. It went on for days! Mr Laine invited everyone to his home and gave them free run of the entire mansion. It was marvellous to gaze upon the 21 Gold Records adorning the walls! On another day Frank joined us for lunch at the Musicians Union Hall and then gave a marvellous and emotional concert, superbly backed by Benny Hollman's big band. The fun just went on and on!

That had been my first trip to the United States. I was impressed by the friendliness, kindness, and warmth of the San Diego people. But Betty, who had never been to the States, hadn't travelled with me. I decided to take her to San Diego for a holiday the following year. It had been twenty years since Betty had last met Frank, at a concert in Dublin. A few months before the trip I phoned Frank to let him know we'd be in town for about twelve days. Any chance we could meet up for a few minutes?

"Sure thing," answered Frank. "It'll be great to see you again. You can stay at our place. We've got plenty of room."

That was kind. We thanked Frank. But we wouldn't dream of imposing ourselves in the household for twelve days. But Frank and his lovely new wife Marcia, whom he married in1999, had us up there almost every day, or, just for a change, taking us to lunch in the singer's favourite restaurant in San Diego's Little Italy section. I'll always remember a comment Frank made as we began lunch in the restaurant. "Hugh, he said, "if I'd wanted to impress you I'd have taken you to a swanky place in the heart of town." He tapped his finger on the gingham-patterned tablecloth. "But right here we get the best food in San Diego!" Now, four years later, Betty and I looked forward to greeting Frank again and to help him celebrate a wonderful 90 years. As a birthday present we'd commissioned our good friend, Bangor artist Tom Heyburn – who is responsible for the art work in this book – to produce a portrait of Frank as he is today. Tom had, at Frank's request, done a black and white portrait for the singer about four years previously. He'd also painted the cover for Frank's *Lyrics By Laine* album. We knew Frank regarded Tom's work highly.

California's San Diego is a beautiful and friendly city. The warm blue waters of the Pacific lap gently in the bay and wash on to miles and miles of golden uncrowded beaches. Palm trees and blazing tropical flowers grow everywhere in a perfectly natural environment – and it's sunshine all the year round. On our last visit with Frank, enjoying an iced tea in his garden high above the ocean and looking down on the resplendent city I asked Frank if he ever travelled abroad for a holiday. He looked at me in mild amusement, gesturing to the sparkling waters in the bay below and the blazing sun and blue sky above. "Where could I go to beat this?" he asked. Sometimes I ask silly questions.

Now I gazed down from the window of our jet as the engines were throttled back and we descended silently through the hills surrounding western San Diego. It would be great to see the lovely city again and to meet dear friends – Frank and

Marcia, Mary-Jo Coombs, Frank's personal assistant, and Benny Hollman, Frank's music director and his wife Dorothy. Benny, of the Benny Hollman Big Band fame, has worked with just about all the greats in show business including Tom Jones, Englebert Humperdinck, Jimmy Durante, and Mel Torme to mention only a few. He's worked with Frank for ten years. Benny told us Humperdinck was a much bigger draw in Las Vegas than Tom Jones – especially among the females! We'd also meet up again with Jimmy Marino, Frank's producer, and Jimmy's bubbly bundle of fun wife Barbara.

As we glided over the red roofs and blue swimming pools of the San Diego suburbs I saw in the distance the sparkling bay and the graceful Coronado Bridge. Then, just a glimpse of the world-famous Coronado Hotel where the beautiful people stay and where Marilyn Monroe, Tony Curtis, and Jack Lemon shot much of their classic picture *Some Like It Hot.* On our last trip Mary-Jo had taken us to the Coronado and showed us the majestic ballroom where Frank and Marcia were married. I was a little awe-struck entering the prestigious establishment kings and queens and presidents sometimes call home. "Don't worry about it," laughed Mary-Jo. "Just pretend you belong!"

Our hotel was the Best Western on Ash Street, just up from the harbour. After freshening up we set out to stroll along the harbour to Seaport Village. Seaport is delightful. It's San Diego's waterfront landmark, set among three distinctive plazas designed to capture the ambience of Old Monterey and traditional Mexico. The Mexican border is only about sixteen miles away, an easy and inexpensive trolley ride to the bustling city of Tijuana. But Tijuana was for another day.

Seaport was a delightful and perfect place to enjoy the balmy evening and to experience the spectacular sunset just happening across the bay. We wandered around the little winding paths among the palms and exotic flowers and seventy five unique little shops and eateries while the moon rose over Loma and bathed the Pacific in her pale light. One of my favourite stores in Seaport is the oddly named The Upstart Crow. It's a delightful coffeeshop-cum-bookshop, crammed from floor to ceiling with good books, great coffees whose lovely aromas never fail to draw me in, and lots of other interesting bits and pieces. I bought a couple of nice and unusual volumes. When I paid for them the owner, recognizing my accent, and after I'd got it in one that he was South African, asked what brought me to San Diego. I told him about Frank's birthday party. "Oh yes," he smiled. "Mr Laine is very well known here. We think a lot of him in San Diego. He often comes in here for books. Usually sits upstairs to browse and make his choices." That was something I often noticed when in San Diego. If you mentioned the name Frankie Laine to anyone in the town – hotel waiter, cabbie, street cleaner, or restaurant owner, the reaction was always the same – "Ah yes. Frankie Laine. Very nice man. He does a lot for our city."

A cycle path runs the length of the quiet lamp-lit walkway from the harbour along to Seaport, a distance of about half a mile. In the evening a dozen or so students – mostly male, but sometimes female – pedal three-wheeled people carriers – something like rickshaws – up and down. We don't usually avail ourselves of them, though the students who ply their trade are always well mannered and friendly. At about ten o'clock, as we began our walk to the hotel, we were hailed by one of the carriers seeking a fare. "No thank you," I called back. Then, remembering we were exhausted and practically out on our feet after the long flight, and that the hotel seemed a long way away, I relented. How much? Ten dollars. Typical Northern Ireland man that I am, and country bred, I don't usually pay the asking price. So we struck a deal at eight dollars, with everybody happy, and travelled home to our hotel in style. It turned out our "driver" had relatives in Cork from where he'd just returned after spending a few weeks there. We slept well that night, with the big San Diego moon hanging in a clear sky silvering the ocean as the Amtrak train mourned through the night on its way to Los Angeles.

The next day Mary-Jo invited us and Rosie Carden,

Chairperson of the U.K. Laine Society and her friend Mair to join her and the rest of the gang – Benny and his wife Dorothy and Jimmy and his wife Barbara, for lunch up at La Jolla – pronounced La Hoya. With a backdrop of green hills ablaze with vibrantly multi-coloured flowers and shrubberies, La Jolla is a sort of extended village snaking along seven miles of the curving Californian coastline. The beaches are clean and empty, and the blue waters lapping them inviting, even for a non-water person such as I. At one point we ambled within touching distance of a couple of dozen seals basking on the rocks. Chipmunks darted in and out among our feet and feasted on the lush greenery which spills right down to the ocean. They're friendly little things, chipmunks, and accepted from my fingers, very politely, a few nuts and other bits and pieces. I noticed the chipmunks when they pulled a shoot of vegetation chewed only at the juicy and nutritious end of the stalk, discarding it when they came near the top of the blade. You don't have to tell chipmunks what's good for them.

Rosie, when buying a little gift in one of the up-market shops railed at the price, I told her to do a bit of wheeling and dealing Irish style with the proprietor. She did, and paid less than she and the proprietor anticipated when she took the goods to the counter!

We lunched at a lovely open-air restaurant overlooking the rolling white-capped waves of the Pacific. The view was perfection; the company even more so. Although most of our friends in the gang work in the music industry, and all very close to Frankie Laine, they are absolutely free of the hangups we sometimes associate with people who earn their living in that business. Just ordinary, kind, warm-hearted friends, who simply could not do enough for us during our twelve day stay. I think they enjoyed our company. We certainly enjoyed theirs. We shared many happy and laughter-filled hours together.

Frankie Laine celebrated his 90th birthday on the 30th March 2003. For Frank's eighty-fifth most of the celebrations for the several hundred friends who attended were held in and around the singer's home. This time, with the maximum seven hundred guests already lined up, and more clamouring to attend, it would have to be different. The U.S. Grant is one of San Diego's plushest hotels, renowned for its turn-of-the-century elegance and old world charm. It looks across to the renowned Gaslamp Quarter, the oldest and most elegant part of town. Western hero – or anti-hero – Wyatt Earp, of O.K. Corral fame, lived just round the corner from the Grant. Burt Lancaster played Earp to Kirk Douglas's Doc Holliday in the 1957 film *Gunfight At The OK Corral.* Laine of course sang the theme song behind the credits and featured the material on his highly successful western album *Hell Bent For Leather.* Frank had been involved in so much western material – once even starring in an episode of *Rawhide* – and had won such world-wide acclaim for his unique interpretation of western ballads it was decided the party should be celebrated in a western theme with cowboy and cowgirl dress acceptable.

Two hours before the party was to begin the Grant's ballroom and ante-rooms were jam-packed with friends who had travelled from all over the world to pay homage to the much loved entertainer. The nice thing about any Laine convention is that everyone knows everyone else – old friends meet again – and the dozens of new fans who always turn up are immediately brought into the fold. A dozen or so tables just off the ballroom were piled high with Frank's albums and videos and books, all personally signed. These, and many of his own personal possessions such as golf clubs, awards, lobby cards etc. would be sold off and auctioned, the entire proceeds going to minister to people in need in and around San Diego – another mark of the singer's generosity. Mary-Jo, dressed in just about the cutest cow-girl outfit you ever did see, helped to sell the product along with Jimmy Marino's wife Barbara and a half dozen mature and beautiful ladies all dolled up in the flapper style of the 1920's.

It was great to meet up again with old friends Pam and Tony Cooper, and to meet for the first time Vicki Lockridge who puts a power of work into running the American Laine Society. Ken Prewitt, another long-time Laine fan made the trip from England despite being confined to a wheel chair. Scotland was represented by "Stormin' Norman" Foster and his wife May from Dumfries.

Frank and Marcia had stayed overnight in the Grant to save driving down from Point Loma on the day of the party. The idea was to relax and take it easy before the whole shingbang got under way. It didn't quite work out that way. The phone began to ring from early morning and the knocks on the door became more and more frequent as well-wishers and media crews clamoured for an audience and interviews. It was hectic. But unknown to everyone Frank had a painful though not serious accident in his room during the night. Now, just before the party began, and when another hundred people had been squeezed into the ballroom, boosting the guest list to eight hundred, news of the accident began to circulate, causing some to fear Mr Laine might not make an appearance. But at two o'clock when Benny Hollman swung into action with his big band and *I Can't Stop Loving You*, everyone relaxed. M. C. Dennis Morgigno welcomed the guests. Then a roar of delighted applause swept the ballroom as Nonagenarian Mr Frankie Laine was introduced to a standing ovation. Everyone rose to acclaim the troubadour, whom we learned later was in quite a bit of pain, but who gave not the slightest hint of it to those who came to help him celebrate. And if there were some striking western outfits on parade among the guests, they were put completely in the shade as Frankie Laine took the stage. The maestro was a striking figure, tall, lean, black trousers, black frock coat, white shirt, bootlace tie and black stetson, looking half his ninety years and evoking memories of all those driving and dramatic western recordings which remain classics and top sellers to this day.

Frank greeted his friends, for his fans are his friends, and thanked them for coming to *another* of his birthday parties. "Some of you may know," he continued, "and some of you may not know I've had quite a severe throat problem for some time, and that has somewhat curtailed my singing. My doctors haven't even allowed me to speak." He chuckled. "Some folk think that's the best thing ever happened!" I knew about the throat problem. I had occasion to telephone the Laine household some months earlier to obtain some information about Frank for a radio feature I was doing on BBC. During the conversation Marcia asked if I'd like to speak to Frank. "But Frank can't talk," I said, well aware the doctors had forbidden him to speak to anyone. "You're right," laughed Marcia, "but he can listen! And I know he'd like to hear from you. And he's got a whistle, so he can respond to your comments!" Typical Frankie Laine. Never a quitter, he simply climbs over the top of his problems, or drives around them. So we had our conversation, with me talking down one end of the line and Frank whistling down the other!

"The doctors tell me it'll be two years before I can sing again the way I used to," Frank informed his birthday audience. "But I told them I can't wait that long. I'll be ninety-two – maybe too old to catch the hit-parade!"

During the delightful Champagne Luncheon of tortilla soup, rolls, chicken salad and birthday cake Jimmy Marino screened, on two large monitors, a twenty minute synopsis of the forthcoming four hour TV documentary *The Frankie Laine Story*. One segment of Frank performing in an Elvis jumpsuit, almost brought the house down! The big show-biz names who paid tribute to Frank included Pat Boone, Michel Legrand, Kay Starr, Terry Moore, Dick Clark, Nat "King" Cole's daughter Maria, John Williams and Patti Page and Jo Stafford. Greetings and congratulations were read from the Mayor of Chicago (where Frank was born), the Governor of California, Gray Davis, and President George W. Bush. Benny Hollman paid tribute to the man he calls "boss". He also mentioned Frankie Laine's generosity in encouraging new talent. The owners of the restaurant where Frank lunches in Little Italy happened to mention to Frank about a young lady just beginning her show-biz career. Her name was Sacha Boutros.They said she was good. Frank did her the honour of inviting her to sing at his party. From a small cafe atmosphere in Little Italy the young lady took the giant step of performing at one of San Diego's top hotels before eight hundred Frankie Laine fans – and turned in a superb version of one of Frank's own hits, *Autumn Leaves.*

Myles Williams, formerly of the New Christie Minstrals, performed a few of Frank's big hits and guitarist Mundell Lowe accompanied his wife on two songs. Benny then introduced one of the legendary names in American music, Mr Herb Jeffries. In his 92nd year, Herb is probably the last surviving member of the original Duke Ellington Orchestra. He spoke highly of his friend Frank – "a humble and beautiful man" and then brought the house down with superb renderings of his two classic hits *Satin Doll* and *Flamingo.* It was marvellous to listen to a quality singer singing quality material at the age of 91! Sad to say, musically speaking, I believe the youngsters of today are suffering from malnutrition. "Listen, kids," smiled Herb to his not exactly teen-age audience. "Don't let them knock you with this old-age business. We've got the advantage. We've seen it. We've done it. And we're still doing it! Remember, the best of everything is old. The best cars. The best cheeses. The best wines. All old. But they go under another title. Classic. Or vintage. That's what we are kids. Classic. And vintage. Tear the word "old" from your dictionary. We don't need it. We're vintage!" Vicki Lockridge of *The Frankie Laine Society of America* honoured Frank in a detailed and well crafted speech before lovely Rosie Carden got to her feet to say how much Frankie Laine was loved by so many people across the world, and how many lives he had touched, not only through his music, but through his kindness and generosity.

As usual Frank was open and available to all who came to his table to greet and congratulate him. The original idea was he would circulate and move among the guests. Because of the accident that wasn't possible. Marcia did a sterling job, doing all the legwork and greeting everyone in her gracious manner. Betty and I would have liked to have gone to Frank's table to say hello.

So would hundreds of others. And many did. But I was very much aware this would be a tiring day for Frank, particularly in view of the discomfort he was in because of the accident. Frank had given us so much of his time through the years I thought it better to hold back and let him enjoy the day in his own way. Tony Cooper and wife Pam, and Rosie, top-notchers in the Laine Society and who always had Frank's ear, felt the same. Anyway, I reckoned if Frank spoke to each of his guests for only one minute, he would still be talking to his fans at six o'clock the following morning. It was impossible. But although we didn't know it then, we would indeed meet up with Frank before our stay at San Diego was over.

The party, a marvellous success, finally broke up at about seven o'clock. Frank had retired to his room for a well-deserved rest, but no one wanted to go home. More chats with old friends, more photographs, more goodbyes. It was hard to leave the wonderful atmosphere that had filled the day. By the time we were ready to depart the place was almost deserted. That's when our dear friend Mary-Jo Coombs asked Betty and I if we'd join her and Benny and Jimmy and the gang for dinner in the Grant's dining room. That was an honour for us. These people not only look after Frankie Laine and his career – they are his closest friends. More than that, they love him. And it shows. But they're our friends too and it was a pleasure to join them for a wonderful dinner. Jimmy Marino arrived at the table a little late. He apologised, saying he'd been sorting out something about Frank with Kay Starr. Kay, of *Rock 'n Roll Waltz* and *Wheel of Fortune* fame, had always been one of my favourite female vocalists, one of the all-time greats, and an artiste who had often appeared with Frank. But I hadn't seen her at the party. I asked Jimmy where she was now. "Just next door, in the lounge," replied Jimmy.

"Do you think she might say hello, if I went in?" I asked.

"Oh sure," answered Jimmy casually. "Kay's a real nice lady."

When I got to the lounge it was empty, except for two ladies who had their back to me. I spoke to a waiter standing just in front of the ladies.

"Excuse me," I said. "Could you tell me if Miss Kay Starr is still in the hotel?"

The young waiter looked at me blankly. "Miss Kay Starr? I'm sorry sir. I don't think I'm familiar with that name."

"Kay Starr," I tried to explain, realizing the young waiter was the wrong vintage, or not vintage at all. "Singer. International recording artiste …"

My voice trailed away as the young man shook his head. "I'm sorry, sir."

"Oh well. Thanks anyway," I murmured, disappointed I had come so close to meeting the great American singer. "She's probably left by now." That's when one of the two ladies turned, smiled into my face, and said sweetly – "Hello. I'm Kay Starr!"

As a writer and broadcaster I'm pretty much at home with the written and spoken word. They come easily to me. Now I was speechless. As a youngster I used to stand around the juke-box in Donaghadee's Joyland Amusement Arcade, listening to Frankie Laine and Kay Starr. Now I gazed into the face of one of the great talents of popular music, not knowing what to say. "Kay," I spluttered. "I grew up with your music, and the music of the nineteen-fifties." That was all I could manage.

"Well," smiled Kay, "you grew up with the best!"

Miss Kay Starr chatted easily with me for ten minutes. When granted an audience with a celebrity it's always good to know when it's time to take your leave. But each time I attempted to say goodbye Kay continued on in conversation. Finally I asked if she would do me the honour of signing an autograph for me. "With the greatest of pleasure," smiled Kay, now a beautiful and unbelievable eighty year old. Now, one of the rudest things you can do is ask for an autograph and not have a pen or even a piece of paper. I had neither. I apologised.

"Don't worry," said Kay happily. "I'll sign my copy of Frank's birthday programme. I can get another." And she did, and posed for photographs and talked of the shows she'd done with Frank and the golden days of popular music when singers were singers and music was music. I went home to the hotel that evening a very happy man. Sometimes you don't even need to have the dream for it to come true.

The Frankie Laine people – Mary-Jo, Benny Hollman and Jimmy Marino and their families were so kind to us every day of our twelve day stay in San Diego, wining and dining us at every opportunity. One afternoon we drove out to Jimmy's house where he very proudly showed us the new pepper tree he'd just planted in his front garden. Jimmy and Barbara's home is also Jimmy's music and recording studio. He's worked with all the top people. Among the dozens of photographs, TV monitors, recording equipment and dozens of Laine videos and c.d's surrounding the walls was a photo of Jimmy with Beatle Ringo Starr and the head of one of Ringo's drums which he had signed for Jimmy. I also spotted on a shelf a very large pair of bright red boxing gloves. I didn't know Jimmy practised the noble art. Anyway, one of the gloves would probably have fitted comfortably over Jimmy's head, never mind his fist. So I asked him about them.

"I was doing a promotional video for Riddick Bowe when he was in training to defend his World Heavyweight boxing title," explained Jimmy. "He signed the gloves and gave them to me." Nice story. Sad ending. Riddick lost his title.

Benny and Dorothy joined us and then the whole gang drove out for a moonlit meal at the Beach House, an open air restaurant where the rolling Pacific beneath our feet crashed on to the grey rocks on the beach. We all indulged ourselves that evening. You should have seen Jimmy put away a Mississippi Mudslinger, a sweet dessert the size of a small bucket!

Betty and I spent a lot of time in Old Town, one of my favourite parts of San Diego. If you want to get a feel of the Old West, Old Town Historic Park is the place to be. Many of the old structures the settlers built in the 1800's have been restored or rebuilt. You can buy a tin of beans or ground coffee at the General Store, visit the Livery Stables and the schoolhouse, buy a Colt 45 and a leather holster to put it in, try on a Sioux war party head-dress, or just browse among the many old shops devoted to Americana and Indian interests. Within Old Town is the Bazaar del Mundo, a maze of south-of-the-border style eating houses and always interesting shops with colourfully dressed Mexican *senoritas* and genuine Mexican music and food. It really is a delightful place to spend a day, and even more romantic by night. Like Seaport Village, and indeed everywhere in San Diego, there is no rush, no hurry, no pressure to buy the product – just kindly well-mannered people, a dusty western atmosphere, and a big blue California sky above. Well, blue by day. Always moonlit by night.

Almost every evening we returned to the enchanting Seaport Village, and once on a very special occasion, with Mary-Jo. The setting red sun had just splashed into the bay as we ambled along and through the little winding paths among the individual shops and along the harbour where the boats with twinkling mast lights silently drifted in and out on the calm waters. Jerry G. Bishop, another friend of Frank's, and a disc jockey on San Diego's K. Pop radio, runs a Greek restaurant in Seaport, almost on the waterfront. Jerry's a nice man and plays the best music. We'd met him a couple of times on our last trip. He's part of the Laine gang. So we thought we'd call in to say hello. Jerry sat behind the counter – as the Americans would say – "like an ordinary Joe" – taking the orders and passing them on to his very efficient staff who prepared the mouth-watering food. I decided since we were in the restaurant we might as well have something to eat. So we ordered. "It's on the house," smiled Jerry.

"No," I answered. "We didn't come in to do that!"

"I know you didn't," grinned Jerry. "But it's still on the house!" We finally agreed to split the bill fifty-fifty. But that again was an indication of the generosity of the people around Frankie Laine. Jerry joined us at our table. We talked about music and life. But mostly about Frank. "He's a tough old bird!" laughed Jerry.

"Ninety years old and he's still going. He's never going to quit!" Jerry's probably correct.

Two or three years ago Frank recorded a great album called *It Ain't Over 'Til It's Over*. All the songs on the album were written by another of Frank's friends, the late Deane Hawley. Every song takes a positive look at growing older and sends out the message there's always more to do in life, more to achieve, and more to enjoy, if you have the right attitude. But you don't have to be old to enjoy the *It Ain't Over 'Til It's Over* album, or to apply its principles.

And we did get to visit Tijuana, just across the border in Mexico. It's a crazy, bustling town, the complete opposite of San Diego. The main street and every side street is just one big conglomeration of souvenir shops and street traders. The Mexicans will literally haul you into their premises – " just for you *senor*, I geeve everything half-price then give you ninety per cent discount!" – "whatever you want *senorita*, I have eet right here!" – "come into my shop *amigos*, and spend your last thousand dollars with me!" Or the classic request, addressed to Betty as she walked along with carrier bags filled to the brim with Mexican souvenirs. "Hey, lady! Come into my store and buy some more junk!" Tijuana is fun and good value and the people are friendly. It's great if you're prepared to let yourself go and join in. Not such a good place to relax! And by the way, if you do go shopping in Tijuana, divide by ten whatever price you're asked. That'll probably be a fair enough amount to pay. And they'll be happy to take your dollars!

A day or two after the birthday party Mary-Jo invited us to drive up to her home further along the balmy Californian coast at Laguna Niguel to see the magnificent flower fields along the way. We'd pass through the Del Mar area where a lot of the greats in the entertainment world have made their home. Del Mar also has a very famous racecourse. Bing Crosby, Jimmy Durante and Al Jolson spent a lot of time and not a few dollars there! Later, at the end of the week, we'd be back here as the guests of Benny

Hollman and the San Diego Musicians Union when the Rancho Santa Fe Big Band under their President and conductor Jack Wheaton played a Spring Fever concert at the Rancho Santa Fe Garden Club. And our presence would even be announced from the stage, eliciting a little wave of acknowledgement from myself! I began to think I could talk myself into getting used to a life in show-business! But today, on the way up to Laguna we'd have a bite to eat at Mary-Jo's favourite little cafe, Proud Mary's (the title of another Laine hit record) overlooking Laguna harbour. Another of the treats here would be to watch the pelicans flying across the bay. We'd first seen them at La Jolla, huge, awkward looking birds, and seemingly belonging to a prehistoric age. We'd also visit the Museum of Music which houses some of Frank's Gold Discs and instruments and material owned by the musical greats from the turn of the last century, and on through the beginnings of rock-n-roll to the present day. Before we set out on the 100 mile drive to Laguna we received a call from Marcia, Frank's wife. Could we spare the time on the way to call up to the house at Point Loma and say hello to Frank? Could we ever! We were touched that Frank, still recovering from his painful accident and a hectic birthday party and with the phone ringing off the hook would take time to make contact and invite us once more to his home. Again, typical of the man.

Mary-Jo drove up the hillside on Kellog and pressed the remote control in the car to open the gates. As we drove through the gates closed behind us and we climbed the twisting driveway leading up the cliff top to Frank's beautiful home. The first time I'd been up to the house, five years earlier, I'd been an emotional bundle of nerves. I was just the little kid who used to live in the sticks at Ballyhay. Now as the car swept up to the front door of the white timbered building overlooking San Diego Bay it was just like popping next door to see a friendly neighbour. Marcia greeted us and invited us to "come on in!"

It was wonderful to meet Frank again. He was seated at the breakfast table in his old sloppy joes and sneakers, casual as ever, and hugging Matt Noir, the jet-black French poodle he loves so dearly. As I moved forward to greet him he looked up and smiled. He knew what was coming. A great big hug. "Be careful, Hugh," he said as he pulled back his shirt to expose a right shoulder and chest a mass of deep black and blue bruises. "This hurts," he grinned. "And it's sure upset my bowling arm," – a reference to his new hobby of ten-pin bowling which he had taken up at the age of eighty-nine. Talk about it ain't over 'til it's over! But we hugged him anyway as he invited us to be seated. It was as if we'd never been away. Frank chatted easily about his birthday party, about music and life, and about the new documentary of his long career in show-business. He enthused about the new album he was working on – twelve tracks of unreleased Laine material.

I'd mentioned to Mary-Jo on the way up to the house it would be best if we stayed only a few minutes. On other visits we'd ambled round the house all day, at Frank's invitation, visiting his music room where he works on all his arrangements, studying the vast and interesting library, the original works of art, which includes work by Bangor's Tom Heyburn, and of course the 21 Gold Discs, framed and hung on the walls. It's a delightful, spacious house, filled with memorabilia and awards from almost sixty years in show business. And we'd seen it all. So this time it would be enough just to greet Frank, wish him well, and thank him again for his kindness through the years. I mentioned to Frank that BBC's Walter Love had asked me to come into the studios immediately I returned home to do a thirty five minute broadcast about the 90th birthday and everything that happened around it. Walter and I had done several previous programmes on Frank, interviewing him live from the house. Frank remembered those features and asked for a tape of the new broadcast to be sent to him.

"Frank," I said, "I've already chosen two of your records, "*Love is a Golden Ring*" and "*My Friend*" to open and close the programme. Is there a particular favourite of your own you'd like us to play?"

Now, bear in mind the last time Mr Laine and I had an in depth discussion about his music was out in his garden almost four years previously. I almost fell from my chair as he leaned toward me, smiled, and said, "Well, Hugh. Why don't you play your own favourite, *These Foolish Things*." That brought tears to my eyes, that this world renowned entertainer, who meets and talks to hundreds, if not thousands of people every year, should recall a little snippet of conversation we shared four years ago.

These Foolish Things comes from Frank's *Torchin'* album produced in 1958 with the Frank Comstock Orchestra. I'm convinced this is the most perfectly performed popular song by any popular singer in the business – bar none. The *Torchin'* album reveals the other side – what many Laine fans consider the true side – of Frankie Laine's talent. Listen if you will to the genuine artistry and sensitivity and superb phrasing as the singer's warm voice lovingly caresses each line of the lyrics in these beautiful recordings which include *A Cottage For Sale, I Cover The Waterfront, Body and Soul, Midnight on a rainy Monday* and *Torchin'* which Frank co-wrote with Al Lerner. Cowboy belters they are not – these are torch songs torn from life's experiences of love and loneliness and performed with such an uncanny depth of feeling by Frankie Laine you feel he is reaching right down inside your innermost being to ensure you experience what he is trying to deliver.

But what's a birthday without a birthday cake! Marcia cut everyone a huge wedge of the super cake and served lashings of hot coffee and tea. What I like about Marcia is she does the cooking and washing up herself. On most occasions! And the last time we visited the house Marcia served up some sumptuous sandwiches which disappeared quickly from the plates.

"How long did it take you to make the sandwiches?" I queried of Marcia.

"About five minutes," chortled Frank, jumping in quick as a flash. "Just as long as it took her to drive down to the deli!" We tucked into the cake and coffee and tea. But I could see Frank was a little tired and I knew he always took a morning nap. I nodded to Mary-Jo it was time to go and let our host rest. But Frank continued talking. When I asked if we could take a photograph for the forthcoming article I'd be doing for the *Newtownards Chronicle* he was ready for action. He very much enjoyed my two previous articles on him which the newspaper had published. "Sure thing," he agreed. He knew I knew my way around the house and the splendid garden overlooking the Pacific. "Where do you want to take the shot?" To save Frank moving too much I suggested he sit in his favourite armchair – his late mother's armchair – at his desk where he worked. "I'll just get my cap," he said, rising to his feet. Frank usually wears his favourite baseball cap with the very true words "Oldie But Goodie" emblazoned on the front.

Betty and I hugged Frank at each side of the chair as Mary-Jo took the pictures. Then we prepared to say goodbye for another time. Because of his injury Frank hadn't yet opened his birthday presents. But he decided to open ours before we left. Our gift was the unique portrait of Frank, as he is today, painted by Tom Heyburn. I'd noticed Tom's previous portrait of Frank taking pride of place as we came into the house earlier. Now the singer's blue eyes sparkled and gleamed as he smiled broadly and gazed at the new work. He was impressed. "Hey! Did Tom do this?" he asked. "Isn't it great! That guy is one heck of a talent," he continued as I nodded in confirmation.

More emotional hugs. More kisses. Then it really was time to go. What precious memories we took away again of the graciousness and kindness of Frankie Laine, caring for and sharing with those around him, as he has done throughout his entire life and career. "Life," Frank once told me, "is good. But it isn't always fair. It isn't always easy." He spoke the truth. But dreams sometimes do come true. Even for a little kid who lived in a tumbledown lamp lit cottage out in the sticks. So, dream your dreams. They just might come true. And maybe, somewhere along the way, if you're lucky, you'll encounter someone whose kindness and generosity and humility shine like a beacon in the rough seas of life. Such a person is Frankie Laine. Frankie Laine, American legend. Frankie Laine, gentleman. Frankie Laine – my friend.

Epilogue – Why I Love Her

"Whatever you're lookin' for," said my granda to me when I was just a wee boy growing up on his farm in Ballyhay near Donaghadee, "you'll find it up in Smithfield Market."

He was right. Although at that time I didn't know what Smithfield Market was or where it was I listened in fascination to my granda's wonderful stories of the things he had discovered in Belfast's old Smithfield. "You can get anything up there," repeated my granda. "Anything from a needle to an anchor!"

As I had never given much consideration to sewing or knitting or embroidery or needlework of any sort, and as there was a distinct lack of boats floating about our fields requiring an anchor – even in the rainy season – I wasn't particularly impressed. But when my granda started to talk about Dutch rabbits and snakes and even monkeys in Smithfield's pet shop and parrots that could talk and canaries that could whistle *Yankee Doodle Dandy*, I sat up and paid notice. My granda said in Smithfield you could buy a gramophone with a box of steel needles and a big pile of shellac records for ten bob, discover a hard to find valve for the wireless, get a battery operated film projector with a load of Charlie Chaplin films for next to nothing and all the books you could ever read in your lifetime for a few pennies each. If you needed a suit of clothes or a pair of boots, a chair to sit on or a picture to hang on the wall – they were giving them away up at Smithfield.

There was no doubt about it. Smithfield was the place to be. And my granda promised to take me there. Many, many times he promised to take up to Belfast and to the Aladdin's cave that was Smithfield. But he never did. As a boy I found all my happiness roaming the fields and lonens of the beautiful Ballyhay countryside, far away from Smithfield.

In my early teenage years I discovered popular music. Most youngsters discover it now before they've left the cradle, and unfortunately it isn't music they find, though it goes under that name. Suddenly all the years of half listening to Donald Peers on the wireless warbling *By a Babbling Brook* and the forces sweetheart Vera Lynn singing *We'll Meet Again* and Sandy McFarlane tearfully delivering *Grannie's Hielan' Hame* began to have an effect upon me. They were great old songs and we all enjoyed hearing them on the wireless when the battery was working. These and other favourites made a great impression on me. Maybe wee boys aren't naturally given to vocal refrain, but I started to sing the old songs as I helped to cut the corn and turn the hay and dug for the ivory white potatoes in the black peat soil. One or two of the farmhouses near us had a gramophone in their parlour and a big pile of shiny black 78rpm records just waiting to be played. Although I caught the occasional glimpse of the parlour and the treasures it contained nobody ever seemed interested in playing the gramophone. It just sat there with its records, a prized piece of furniture, and wonderful music and singers and songs silently sealed in the black wax discs and doomed never again to be heard in the still country air.

I wanted a gramophone! Oh how I longed for a wind-up gramophone and a collection of records which I could play over and over again, as often as I wanted, and when I wanted. That was the beauty of the gramophone. You didn't have to wait and hope your favourite record was played on the wireless which usually didn't work anyway because the battery needed charged. With a gramophone you could slip the record out from its paper sleeve – being careful not to let it fall or it would shatter into a dozen pieces – place it on the turntable, wind up the gramophone, lower the arm with the steel needle and away you'd go. Instant music and song, and you could even adjust the volume by opening or closing the doors of the cabinet which housed the cloth covered speaker where the sound came out.

But my granda wasn't so fond of music he was going to splash out hard earned money on a gramophone. So when the wireless was working, I carried the words and tunes of my favourite singers and songs and kept them alive by singing them all day long – except of course when I was at school. At school there was no way was I going to admit I liked any type of music or singing of any sort and risk getting myself hauled into some sort of choir. My music was strictly for my own entertainment and happiness.

However, as I have said before, dreams sometimes do come true. One dark winter night my uncle Francie, who lived in Newtownards, arrived at our little cottage in his old Ford Prefect motor-car. That was excitement in itself – a car – and especially my uncle arriving unannounced at our wee place on a stormy black night.

"Come and see what I've got for you!" my uncle called to my little sister Ann and I as we opened the cottage door and looked out by the light of the hurricane lamp. "Come and see!"

Childhood years in the country just after the war followed one after the other without anything special or out of the ordinary happening. But this was definitely special and very much out of the ordinary. As my uncle fussed about and undid the ropes holding some sort of big black cabinet on the roof of the car I suddenly realised what it was.

"It's a gramophone!" I shouted to Ann as I swung the lamp about excitedly. "It's a gramophone!"

And gramophone it was – not a new one of course, a big Parlophone cabinet job with opening and closing doors and a turntable which spun automatically when you lowered the tone arm on the record. It had boxes of needles to play the records – all sorts of needles for your listening requirements, soft tone, medium tone, and loud tone. You simply undid the little screw and inserted the needle of your choice. Each of the needles, what ever the tone, was extremely similar in appearance and feel to an inch long nail with a point that would cause blood to spurt from your finger if you happened to show carelessness in the handling of it.

The gramophone was manhandled into the house and stood in a corner – not in the parlour for we didn't have a parlour – but in what we called the kitchen – the room we lived in. Our gramophone wouldn't be an ornament. It would be played. Then the records were carried in – dozens of them, Decca, Brunswick, The Winner, Regal-Zonaphone, His Masters Voice and others I'd never heard of. What excitement as Ann and I took turns in winding up the spring and playing them over and over again. What titles! The Little old Mud Cabin on the Hill, The Old Rustic Bridge, Grannie's Hielan' Hame, The Old Pine Tree, The Laughing Policeman, Two Lovely Black Eyes and so many more. How many happy, happy hours we enjoyed around that old second-hand gramophone.

But after a year or two I began to tire of Grannie's Hielan' Hame and the Old Pine Tree. Now there were new singers on the wireless – even singers from America – and their songs and music began to beckon me. I remember the whole summer of 1956 I stooked the corn and built the haystacks while crooning Teresa Brewer's big hit recording *A Tear Fell.* I was just turned fourteen but the emotional delivery of Teresa's performance on that recording wasn't lost on me. The hit songs from top quality entertainers like Eddie Fisher, Guy Mitchell, Kay Starr, Nat

'King' Cole, Frankie Laine and Perry Como came one after the other and it seemed they would never cease. Frankie Laine was my favourite. I wanted to own his records, as well as all the others, to play on my gramophone when I felt like it. And you never could tell, maybe there would come a time when the hit-parade would be made up with a different quality of singers and songs than I was enjoying now. Maybe not as good. These great singers and great songs couldn't last forever. I had to get these recordings now.

But where was a fourteen year old country schoolboy going to find five shillings and eleven pennies to buy even one of the prized records, let alone every one of them. It couldn't be done. But eventually I persuaded my grandaprents we really did have to move with the times and buy a new record. Reluctantly they gave me the money to go to Newtownards to buy a new recording. There was one stipulation. The record had to be Belfast's Ruby Murray singing *Softly,Softly*. I didn't mind that. Ruby was a nice singer and I turned in a fair performance of *Softly,Softly* myself when I was cleaning out the henhouse. *Softly,Softly* was the first record I ever bought.

By the time I had started work and had a shilling or two in my pocket, the thing I greatly feared had happened. All my favourites singers were slipping from the hit parade and the records I wanted so badly a few years earlier were no longer available in the shops now I had the money to buy them. That's when I remembered what my granda had told me years before – "If there's anything you're lookin' for, you'll find it in Smithfield." Well, maybe Smithfield would have some of the marvellous 1950's records.

They did. Hundreds of them, piled one on top of the other in six foot high piles in dozens of dingy little second-hand record stalls. Initially I went there to look for Frankie Laine's Columbia and Philips recordings. I found them, at sixpence or a shilling each, as well as loads of other deleted but superb recordings. I must have shifted tons of black shellac and wax, lifting the first record from the top of the pile, examining it, laying it on the floor if I didn't need it, putting the next record on top of that and so on until I had record by record transferred the pile of discs in the shop from one position to another. Once I found *A Four Legged Friend* sung by my boyhood cowboy hero Roy Rogers. The man who owned the stall wouldn't sell it to me. No matter how much I offered he wouldn't sell it. He grabbed it from me, which indicated he hadn't even know it was in the pile, and wouldn't let go. He probably knew what he was doing. For almost forty five years I've searched for another copy of *A Four Legged Friend.* I've never found one. But I carted my treasures I found through the years on the bus to my new home in Newtownards where my wife rolled her eyes heavenward as I entered beaming from ear to ear. Women just don't understand about these things.

Smithfield really did have everything you needed. The strange thing is, as I reflect on my regular Saturday morning jaunts to its junk covered aisles, I always went there to find deleted records. I loved reading and books just as much as I loved music. But I never browsed through any of the thousands of volumes of the written word piled up all over Smithfield. I wish I had the opportunity to do it now. And yet later, as I hopefully honed my writing skills, records and writing and old Smithfield came together to enable me, without any planning, to write a small piece which has become extremely popular with my storytelling and radio audience.

It happened as I browsed through the long-playing albums in McBurney's Premier Record Store, just before old Smithfield burned to the ground. In the Country section I suddenly came upon an album by screen legend John Wayne. Now I was a big John Wayne fan. But I didn't know John Wayne could sing. So I bought the album and took it home and discovered John Wayne couldn't sing! On this fine album entitled *Why I Love Her* Wayne recited ten poems extolling the virtues and beauties of his beloved America and it's citizens. He did it well, and especially the title track whose words on the sleeve were credited to one John Mitchum. I was beginning at that time to get a little breakthrough in my own writing career. I wasn't then, nor do I now lay any claim to be a poet. But I wondered if I could do something similar to that which John Mitchum had done – but in my case write a poem about Northern Ireland, Southern Ireland – the whole of Ireland – things that were important to me, and maybe to other people. I scribbled down fifteen verses exactly as they came to me. I broadcast the result on Gerry Anderson's radio programme. It was so well received I had to return for two more consecutive mornings to repeat it. And of course I broadcast and discussed the piece on Walter Love's *Love Forty* programme. It's the poem with which I finish all my Storytelling Evenings.

For me, many dreams have indeed come true. I've been fortunate enough to travel to some beautiful and perhaps not too accessable places on this earth, meeting people who are very dear to me. They all hold a very precious place in my heart. But when all is said and done, the old adage 'Home is where the heart is' is very true indeed. The bulk of my published writings extol the beauties and the unique characters and rich humour which are to be found in our own dear land. As a little tribute to a few of them I close this volume with the little piece inspired by the words of John Mitchum and the voice of John Wayne as they were discovered in old Smithfield Market, the place, as my granda said, "you can find anything you're lookin' for."

Why I Love Her

You ask me why I love her, this land of mine,
So I lift my pen and write a line,
To show you why I love her so,
Why the people and the beauty of this land make my heart glow.

Have you ever stopped to rest at Kerry's Ring?
Have you ever heard John McCormack sing?
Did you ever thumb a lift to Portrush,
Then have to get out and push?

Have you ever been to Newtownards town,
And seen the Harvest Fair?
Have you ever sung *My Wild Irish Rose*,
Or walked where the River Shannon flows?

D'you remember when a wee Irish player called Barry,
Arranged for Sean Thornton and Mary Kate Danaher to marry?
Have you ever fished for blockin in a boat off Donaghadee?
Did ever a wee Irish colleen sit upon your knee?

Were you ever offered a cup of tay,
Or asked to stop a while and stay?
Listen to the crack of some oul' country-man,
Or even eat soda-bread, dipped in a pan?

Did you ever kiss the Blarney Stone,
Or gaze across the Bangor Bay, alone?
Have you ever seen an Irish sunset,
Or dug for turf in winter, cold and wet?

Have you ever looked at our fields so green,
Johnny Cash wrote a song – said they were the finest he'd ever seen.
Did you ever hear Danny Blanchflower say
"Hullo there," – his way?

Have you ever been to Helen's Tower
And watched the ascending of the lark?
Have you ever read George Bernard Shaw,
Or gazed at Galway Bay, in perfect awe?

Did you ever go to see James Young?
Have you heard the songs of Percy French sung?
Did you ever climb to the top of Scrabo's famous Tower,
Or maybe stop, to pick the buckie rose's flower?

Did you ever see George Best kick a ball,
Or wear the Shamrock, unique and small?
Did you ever hear wee Rinty sing,
That night, when he was King?

Have you ever been to Killarney's lakes?
Have you heard the sound a lambeg makes?
Have you ever heard Galway play the flute,
Or an old Irish mother say, "cast not a cloot?"

Did you ever climb the Mournes so high,
Or listen to the winds at Mallin, sigh?
Did you ever see *The Quiet Man*,
Or tell a yarn like only an Irishman can?

Did you ever listen to Barney McCool
Tell you an oul' yarn on a milkin' stool?
Did you ever browse through Smithfield Square,
Before they had a big fire there?

Do you remember when a wee girl called Murray
Sang *Softly Softly* without any hurry?
Have you ever heard McNamarra's band?
Have you ever really seen our green and pleasant land?

You ask me why I love her,
This land of my birth?
Well, maybe it's just because in her,
I see, everything, that is me.

Dear Reader

I hope you've have enjoyed this publication from Ballyhay Books. It is one of a growing number of local interest books published under this imprint including Hugh Robinson's book *Back Across the Fields of Yesterday* and John O'Sullivan's *Belfast City Hospital, a Photographic History.*

To see details of these books as well as the beautifully illustrated books of our sister imprint, Cottage Publications, why not visit our website at **www.cottage-publications.com** or contact us at:–

Laurel Cottage
15 Ballyhay Rd
Donaghadee
Co. Down
N. Ireland
BT21 0NG

Tel: +44 (0)28 9188 8033

Timothy S Johnston

Ballyhay Books